C000258283

CONTENTS

ILLUSTRATIONS

FOREWORD

A considerable part of the annual output of the agricultural industry in the United Kingdom today is in the form of animal products, of which milk and dairy produce contribute a major share. If the full potential of the dairy cow is to be realised, it is essential that those responsible for her day-to-day care are not only fully aware of all aspects of rearing and management, but also possess an understanding of the diseases to which she is prone, their prevention and cure.

Since this book first appeared, the need for such a text has become even greater; replacement costs have increased very appreciably and feed costs have spiralled; yield expected per cow lactation has risen, and the individual herdsman has ever greater numbers of cows to look after. Furthermore, in 1973 we have seen the world protein shortage become a reality—an event that is bound to necessitate changes in feeding practice and possibly, as a consequence, create further problems in the maintenance of the cow's health and productivity.

Knowledge concerning all aspects of dairy cow husbandry is continually expanding, and in introducing this eighth edition of Dr Barron's book, I would like to compliment the author and the publisher for endeavouring to provide as up to date a text as possible.

August, 1973

D. G. ARMSTRONG
Professor of Agricultural Biochemistry, The University, Newcastle-upon-Tyne

AUTHOR'S PREFACE

(to First and Subsequent Editions)

THERE is a bond of sympathy between veterinary surgeons and those who care for animals, born of their combined struggle to save and heal. It is in the hope of welding this bond more firmly that I have written this book.

Such a lot can be done on the farm—in management to prevent disease and in first-aid to control it—to ensure freedom from illness and better health for our cattle. All that is wanted is a better understanding of the factors that cause disease.

This understanding is eagerly sought. I know that from my acquaintance with farmer-and-herdsman audiences. After a hard day's struggle with nature they have gathered in village halls and pubs, anxious to learn anything and everything that would make them better stockmen.

To those audiences I am grateful. They have taught me much by their questions and criticisms; they have given me a proper respect for the hardships and difficulties of farming.

I hope this book will serve them well. It will not make them into veterinary surgeons, but it will, I trust, give them—and all dairy farmers and herdsmen who read it—a better understanding of the veterinary side of their job and a wider knowledge of what can be done on the farm in the fight against disease.

NORMAN S. BARRON

Reading

AUTHOR'S PREFACE

To have arrived at a tenth edition is cause for gratification. To think that so many farmers may have been helped in their struggle to achieve more efficient milk production, with cleaner milk and healthier herds, is a matter for quiet reflection.

When money is scarce and prices tight, officialdom glibly advises greater efficiency—and to a considerable degree British dairy farmers have accepted this challenge. The advice was, of course, largely irrelevant but the unused cane in the cupboard stirs the laggard and does good without pain.

National support for the retention of the MMB reflects the interest in the overall co-ordination of our industry, and their help in many fields, including mastitis and the valuable cell-count test backed up by veterinarians, is a welcome reflection of that enthusiasm. Brucellosis is on the way out (another example of farmer co-operation), and warble fly has a short span if modern precautions are taken. And infectious bovine rhinitis and any new hazard will hopefully have a short life. This book points the way.

NORMAN S. BARRON

CHAPTER I

HERD MANAGEMENT FOR HEALTH

DISEASE in livestock is costing the farmers in this country about £150,000,000 annually. Averaged out for every farm, this could mean a loss of £300–£400 a year.

The dairy farmer takes a very heavy share of this loss. If you check up on your losses for the year, you will probably find that they cost you £200–£250.

Your veterinary surgeon's bill was, I hope, nowhere near £200. But you must remember that every time you called upon his services you were losing money in other ways – through loss of milk sales from abortion, sterility or mastitis, through loss of growth in young stock (which can only be made up by heavier feeding and may, in fact, reduce potential yields), through loss of time and labour in every case of illness, and possibly by loss through death.

When all that is added up you will see that my estimate of £200 to £250 per farmer is not far out. It is a loss which should be avoided.

A further point is that every loss you suffer in this way is a loss to the nation – in food; a loss that we can ill afford.

17

It applies to all diseases of livestock. They reduce production and profit.

NOTIFIABLE DISEASES

Some diseases – such as anthrax, foot-and-mouth and rabies – come under the direct supervision of the Animal Health Branch of the Ministry of Agriculture. These diseases are what is known as "scheduled" and are notifiable by the owner on *suspicion* alone. Contact should be made with the local police station.

The full list of such diseases is:

Anthrax; cattle plague; rabies; glanders; contagious bovine pleuro-pneumonia; foot-and-mouth disease; epizootic lymph-angitis; sheep scab; swine fever; certain forms of mange in horses, asses and mules; tuberculosis (certain forms only); fowl pest. It is also illegal to expose a cow in a public place, *e.g.* a market, within six weeks of its having slipped a calf.

However, the officers of the Animal Health Branch have a broader function to perform. Their problem is that of animal health in its widest sense and their horizon is continuously expanding. Through them many schemes are executed. They play a large part in the control of brucellosis, for instance, and keep a check on salmonellosis.

As evidence of this it is only necessary to refer to the success achieved by the tuberculosis eradication scheme. The herds of England, Scotland and Wales are officially free of the disease, and the marked improvement in the health of our dairy herds is clearly evident.

ADVICE TO FARMERS

Within this same branch is the Veterinary Investigation Service (part of the old advisory service until October 1st, 1946) with regional laboratories now under the umbrella of ADAS where diagnosis is done to help veterinary practitioners to arrive at an opinion or to further some disease-control campaign.

The veterinary officers of this service, through lectures and demonstrations, play a large part in bringing to the notice of the farmer modern developments in the control of disease.

Like the officers of the AHB they gather information and carry out experimental work designed to solve some of the more serious problems of livestock disease in conjunction with research institutes.

This brings us to the veterinary surgeons themselves. We shall always need an adequate number of them if a full service is to be given to farmers. They are well trained and versed in dealing with the food-producing animals, their diseases, habits and needs. Many are now specialising in particular animals.

But do you always call in your veterinary surgeon when you should? Do you give him a chance to get going early? Or do you first fly immediately to your pet remedy – which may in fact be a mild purgative and have no specific curative value? And then wait until things have got bad and a little beyond you?

Such an action may cause you to lose a valuable animal by delaying diagnosis and proper treatment.

If you are managing your herd efficiently and breeding constructively, your stock is valuable. It becomes even more valuable as your herd develops. That is a sound reason for calling veterinary aid when necessary – and calling it early. Treatment is an insurance and can be the means of avoiding much loss, and expert advice is always worth paying for.

The "medicine bottle" mentality is deeply ingrained in us all. The sight of one in the hand when a cow is sick may give us confidence, but how often does it end up on the cowhouse window-sill – only partly used!

Medicines have their place and probably always will have. But the afflictions that harass the dairy herd and cut profits are, many of them, herd problems and not individual-cow problems. Bottles of medicine are not the cure.

That is where the trained men, the specialist and the research workers come to your aid and, through your own veterinary surgeon, apply scientific knowledge to your problems. It is their job to find and apply the cure. Plan your future policy with your vet and introduce preventive measures in time. Important matters to consider are, for example, vaccination against salmonella in calves, the Brucellosis control scheme, design of calf houses and isolation boxes for the same, the use of gamma globulin in controlling calf scour, routine pregnancy diagnosis and controlled breeding plans.

SPOTTING WHEN "SOMETHING IS WRONG"

Primarily, however, the control of disease in cows and calves is in the stockman's and dairy farmer's hands.

After years of association with animals, a good stockman develops an uncanny ability in spotting when "something is wrong". His sense for this is often more acute than that of the specially-trained veterinary surgeon.

This is an ability that should be cultivated. It is your opportunity to reduce losses through disease.

It is easy to tell when a cow is really ill, but it may then be too late to apply a simple remedy to check disease which, if contagious, may already have been passed to others. And the longer treatment is delayed, the slower will be recovery.

It requires quite a bit of experience to know when a cow is off colour. At first it is not even a question of pulse or respiration, failure to cud, or a fall in milk. It is probably just an impression or a look in the eye.

It is that first indication of disease or disorder that you want to be able to spot. Sensing that "something is wrong" and acting immediately will prevent more trouble, a bigger veterinary bill and a greater loss of milk.

TEN POINTS TO WATCH

Let these ten points be your guide:
1. The look of the eyes.
2. The way the head is held or the ears moved.
3. The nature of the breathing.
4. The "feel" of the skin.
5. Appearance of the droppings.
6. Appearance of the urine.

7. Variation in gait.
8. Cessation of feeding and cudding.
9. Fall in milk yield.
10. Appearance of milk.

A slight departure from normal, so long as it is not associated with any natural physiological functions such as the presence of heat, or a necessary environmental change, in any of these matters should strike a warning note. It is the danger signal to watch for.

So you should start off by gaining as much experience as possible of the various features that make "a picture of health" in a cow or calf.

STUDY YOUR STOCK

Study the normal habits of your stock – as individuals. Back up your observations with a little private investigation. It is a fascinating and helpful study.

This book has been specially written to help you in this way. It will deal with each disease in detail, explaining its causes, how it affects cows, how it spreads and, more especially, how it can be avoided or controlled.

CHAPTER II

CALVING DOWN A COW

IT is fitting to begin by dealing with the needs of a cow at calving time. This is a vital period – for her and the calf.

And there is a lot that you can do at this time to prevent trouble and disease.

In the first place you want to be sure that you have a proper record of service dates. On that will hinge many of the actions you will have to take, such as drying-off, steaming-up and preparing for the actual calving.

Normally a cow carries a calf, on an average, 285 days; but there is some variation – perhaps a week or ten days one way or the other – in certain cows, seasons or herds, largely through the influence of feeding and management. A quick method of calculation is to count back three months from a year after the day of service and add one week.

With the expected calving date in mind you can plan to give the cow all the attention she needs during the last two vital months.

IMPORTANCE OF DRY PERIOD

The first essential is that she should have an adequate dry

period – a rest from the job of milk production, for at least eight weeks.

For her own health she needs this rest; at the same time it enables her to build up food reserves such as vitamin A which she can pass on in her colostrum together with antibodies against disease which are so important to give the calf a healthy start.

PRECAUTIONS AGAINST MASTITIS

At the drying-off stage you should take certain precautions against disease. If the cow has had mastitis or if there are other mastitis-infected cows in your herd it is wise to ask your veterinary surgeon to inject a long-acting penicillin into each of her quarters after the final milking.

This should prevent a build-up of the common mastitis organisms which might otherwise develop unnoticed while the udder is not being handled.

Another danger is summer mastitis – an unpleasant disease that is all too frequently found in heifers and in freshly-calved animals. It can be fatal; it almost certainly means the loss of any infected quarters.

SEALING THE TEATS

Flies seem to play an appreciable part in its spread, and for this reason sealing the teats to stop infection from passing up the teat canal is a good practice.

First, clean the teats thoroughly with methylated spirits, then either paint them (particularly the orifices) with collodion solution or apply it by dipping each teat in an eggcup filled with the solution. It dries quickly and, properly applied, should remain an effective seal for at least three weeks, and it should be repeated when necessary until calving time is reached.

Heifers will not need – as a routine measure – preventive antibiotic injections into the udder, but you should certainly seal their teats about two months before calving.

Care should be taken, too, in choosing the field for your down-calvers.

At all costs avoid low-lying pastures infested with flies. Try

23

and select a paddock near to the farm in case of trouble, but beware of those "home" paddocks that have never been ploughed and are likely to be full of pests and disease.

SEE DOWN-CALVERS DAILY

Next, make it a regular practice to see down-calving cattle every day during their dry period.

Watch them carefully for a few minutes, look for any odd action and be particularly suspicious if a cow isolates herself from the rest of the herd. It may be a sign of approaching calving but it can often be the first outward sign that "something is wrong."

Apart from this daily check-up it is wise to handle your down-calvers at least twice a week – more frequently if you are in an area where summer mastitis is prevalent.

Bring them into the cowhouse and tie them up. Handle their udders and look especially for any uneven swellings or signs of pain and discomfort.

This is not just advice of perfection. It is worth putting into practice for it may save you much expense and trouble.

Your heifers will respond to the treatment by being easier to handle and well accustomed to the cowhouse by the time they calve.

KEEP THEM CONTENTED

You can make practical use of the time absorbed by feeding heifers and cows their steaming-up ration while they are tied up. You can also apply each time a fly repellent as an additional safeguard against summer mastitis infection and against "gadding". This will keep them more contented – an important consideration at this stage.

With regard to steaming-up you will no doubt follow the customary practice of beginning about six weeks before calving and steadily increasing the ration until about a week before calving is due when this should have reached anything from 8-16 lb (3·6–7·2 kg) a day according to the expected yield of the animal. It could with advantage be slightly reduced until calving, to prevent the bag from becoming too full and tense at calving time. The normal milk production ration is quite satisfactory.

From a veterinary point of view begin with small amounts and increase steadily. Make sure that the ration contains proper mineral supplements and ensure that the cow has vitamin-rich foods – such as best hay, silage or dried grass – so essential for her own and her calf's health. Cake can be obtained which will provide for the mineral (including trace elements) and vitamin needs of the animal – with the vitamins in a stabilised form so that they will not deteriorate in the presence of the trace elements (nor be affected by any rancidity). Food must be fresh and palatable, and not dusty.

QUESTION OF PRE-MILKING

Near calving time the udder will become markedly distended, hard and tense, and actual signs of pain may be seen. The cow will straddle her hind legs, move uneasily from side to side and occasionally glance backwards.

Some farmers make it a rule not to touch the udder at this stage or give it more than a gentle massage. But there is no harm in easing off each quarter by drawing off some of the contents. Only do this however if there is evidence of discomfort or pain – for example, constant paddling of the hind legs, looking round at hind quarters and an unduly hot and hard udder.

The point to remember is that once this practice is started it encourages secretion. Therefore it must be continued, or else the discomfort quickly returns. But on each occasion draw off no more than is necessary to ease the discomfort.

At first the fluid is water-coloured or straw-coloured and rather sticky; later it changes to normal milk if the practice is started sufficiently early before calving.

Whether you milk before calving or not it is a good plan to massage the udder gently as it begins to fill with milk. But take care that whenever you handle an udder your hands have been thoroughly washed and disinfected. Tests have shown that streptococcal mastitis can be passed to heifers at this time by unhygienic methods.

INDOOR OR OUTDOOR CALVING

It is often recommended that cows are best left to calve out-of-doors. Where buildings are poor and cannot be properly disinfected, that may be right.

But it is well to remember that those "home" paddocks, so handy to the buildings, can be just as great a source of infection as dirty loose boxes.

Ideally you cannot better a brick or concrete loose box with a smooth floor and cement-rendered walls. Clean it thoroughly after each calving, use disinfectant solution for swilling down and you will considerably reduce the risk of infection to the next cow and calf. Use a pressure spray followed by washing with sodium carbonate (four ounces (113 g) to the gallon (4·5 litres) of hot water) and allow to dry out thoroughly before re-use.

But the cow needs to be accustomed to this box before she calves. Bring her to it at least three or four days before the event and ensure that she has some exercise each day.

EFFECT ON COLOSTRUM

The point about getting a cow used to her calving premises is important. It has a bearing on the disease-preventing qualities of her colostrum.

Whilst the importance of colostrum for the newly-born animal has long been recognised, only recently have its different fractions been analysed and their separate qualities determined.

Colostrum is a valuable substance. It is highly digestible containing phospho-proteins and casein; it has a high fat content and so has a laxative effect; vitamin A is concentrated in the fat, and it will contain antibodies against disease, especially certain coliform organisms to which the dam has been exposed.

These are qualities I shall be emphasising again in the chapter on calf rearing; the important point is that very valuable antibodies are associated with the euglobulin fraction of the protein. These have the ability to cope with disease-causing coliform bacteria and greatly help to protect the calf against the most prevalent form of scour – which is caused by these bacteria.

But the antibodies will only cope with the particular strains of *E. coli* with which the cow has been in contact during the last few months before calving.

Therefore, when a cow on the point of calving is moved to new quarters there is a risk that the antibodies she will give in her colostrum, whilst being appropriate to the strain of *E. coli* present in her previous abode, may be ineffective against the strain of *E. coli* in her new surroundings.

It is an important point to watch. Some veterinary authorities regard it as so vital that they strongly suggest farmers should not buy cows on the point of calving or new-born calves because of the risks attendant in moving them to new premises.

FEEDING BEFORE CALVING

Two or three days before calving ease off the steaming-up concentrates. See that the bowels are free; if insufficiently laxative, offer bran mashes.

It is suggested in some quarters that, to reduce the risks of excessive udder engorgement and the need for pre-milking, the orthodox steaming-up ration might be better if the protein content were reduced and the overall energy raised.

Small amounts of molasses could be mixed with food and are mildly laxative; but salts, especially if a big dose is given, are purgative. Care should be taken not to give a full dose of any purgative substance during the last two months of pregnancy. Otherwise abortion may result.

One final point; if the cow is a third, fourth or fifth calver, and she has previously had milk fever, then I think it is a wise precaution to see that she has a calcium borogluconate injection within 12 hours before calving.

This can be repeated a few hours after calving if there are indications of a relapse. Fuller reference to the control of this disease is made in chapter IX

WHEN THE COW CALVES

Now we come to calving itself.

First, leave the cow free. If she is tied, she may calve with no-one in attendance and she may tread on the calf or crush it against the wall. Should she herself go down she may hang herself – it is not easy to undo a chain-tie with half-a-ton (0·5 tonne) of cow weighing on it! Therefore tie her to her chain by a piece of string which can easily be cut.

Secondly, you can do some good by washing down the cow's bearings with a mild disinfectant solution before the calf actually appears. Certain scour-causing organisms may be present and it is well to safeguard the calf from these infections as far as possible.

Some prefer to leave nature to take its course at calving. That is not a bad plan. It is certainly better than harmful interference.

But there is always a risk that something may go wrong that could be put right and save one or both lives. Because of the increasing value of stock today, it is now more usual to attend calving and give what help may be necessary.

SIGNS TO LOOK FOR

The signs of approaching calving are well-known. They begin with increasing uneasiness, mooing and irregular movements; the vulva becomes enlarged, congested and flabby; the ligaments on either side of the tail head loosen so that a fist can be placed in each hollow – this, in general, should forecast calving within 12 to 24 hours; there is spasmodic straining and the cow walks with difficulty, often looking round at her own flank.

Then, immediately before the actual calving, the water bladder appears and soon afterwards a nose or foot, then two feet, the whole head and then the shoulders. Once the shoulders – the broadest part – are through there should be no further difficulty.

Just a word about the water bladder or "bag." The purpose of this is to dilate the womb and passage and make things easier for the calf to come. Also the fluid that it contains acts as a shock absorber for the calf and a lubricant to the parts.

Therefore I consider it best not to rupture this bag unless help with calving is obviously necessary.

WHEN HELP IS NECESSARY

How can you tell when help is necessary? In general if a calf is not born within an hour of the appearance of the water bag or within an hour of regular straining, then veterinary advice should be sought.

Manipulation of the calf at this stage is easier and less likely to be followed by fatality than if left longer. Further, a veterinary surgeon is best able to decide whether to help immediately or leave the cow a little longer. And his presence will most certainly be necessary if – as sometimes happens – the hormones responsible for relaxing the neck of the womb and for expelling the calf, fails to function. In such cases stilboestrol injections may be necessary followed later by pituitrin to assist expulsion.

Where help is given there are certain precautions you should observe. The most important is absolute cleanliness.

Always have available plenty of soap and hot water and lubricating oils containing carbolic or other antiseptic agents. Make sure that any rope used has been previously sterilised. Nylon ropes are particularly useful in this aspect – they can be more satisfactorily sterilised than hemp ropes.

Wear a rubber apron if you have one. Clean your hands and arms and oil them well. And those finger nails! They should be thoroughly scrubbed and have no sharp corners.

Even when the calf is properly presented, labour may last many hours. But, once the calf begins to come, its passage should not be too slow or it may die of suffocation. It can be assisted by gentle traction and by easing back the passage walls with the hands.

If progress is steady, there is no need for interference. Gentle assistance, pulling only when the cow labours, is all that is necessary.

ABNORMAL CALVINGS

In most calvings the position of the calf is normal. But there can be many presentations that make it difficult or impossible for the cow to calve without assistance.

Some of these are so complicated that it is absolutely essential to call professional assistance. Others, such as shown in the accompanying illustrations, may need only slight manipulation which an intelligent layman can often perform.

You should start by satisfying yourself that any feet that have appeared belong to the same calf and not to two different calves. As a precaution it is a good idea to attach a calving rope to the first foot that appears.

If you find that both feet belong to the same calf you have then to decide whether they are forelegs or hind legs. This is easily found out – the fetlocks and the knee joint of the forelegs bend the same way; with hind legs the hocks bend the opposite way to the fetlocks.

A good way of avoiding subsequent difficulties is to use coloured nylon calving ropes and to plan their use according to a colour system – for example, yellow for hind legs, red for forelegs.

If both the legs in the passage are forelegs and you can feel the calf's head resting on them, then presentation is quite normal and delivery should be straightforward.

But any pulling should be in a slightly downward direction and care should be taken that the ropes do not cut the flesh of the birth canal.

WHEN FORELEG IS BACK

If the hoofs are not clear of the cow, cup a hand over them until they are: this will prevent any injury to the vaginal wall. Perhaps the most common abnormal presentation is when the foreleg is back. In this case the head has to be pushed back to allow the leg to be drawn up. Then calving should be normal.

In cases where the water bag has burst and tissues are dry, apply an obstetric ointment (liquid paraffin will do) to the lips of the vulva, to the walls of the passage and to whatever parts of the calf are in the passage. This will facilitate delivery.

If the presentation is what is called a "breech," with the calf

NORMAL AND ABNORMAL CALVINGS

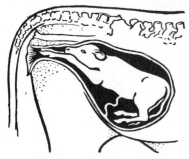

NORMAL PRESENTATION

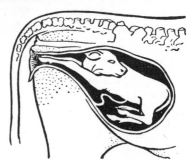

HEAD TWISTED BACK

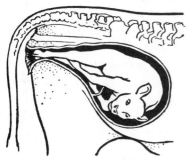

HIND LEGS FIRST

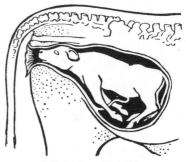

FORELEGS BACK

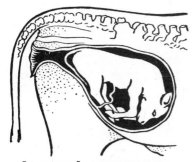

"BREECH" PRESENTATION

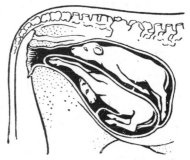

TWINS: *one with head back*

coming backwards, then some rotation of the fore-part of the calf may be necessary before any attempt is made to deliver it – especially if the head is presented between the hind legs as it sometimes is.

In such cases as these a veterinary surgeon may need to resort to spinal anaesthesia to prevent the cow from straining against his efforts.

HEAD TWISTED BACKWARDS

If the head or neck is twisted backwards to one side or th, other, then it must be straightened out before any traction is applied to the legs.

But at all times when attempting to correct a calf's presentation you must remember these important facts:

1. The back of the hand must always be between that part of the calf which is being manipulated and its mother's womb. Thus a foot or nose should always be moved cupped in the palm.

   A rupture of the womb could lead to sterility and possibly to the cow's death. A tear between the birth passage and rectum passage could form what is known as a fistula through which dung would pass into the birth passage and contaminate it, leading to infertility, either through the contamination or by deflecting the penis at time of service.

2. Utmost cleanliness must be observed by using – I repeat – soap, hot water and plenty of antiseptic oils. Far too much sterility is caused through infection introduced into the cow's womb at calving time.

3. The rope must always be in such a position that, when traction is applied, it will not cut or rub the birth canal.

PROFESSIONAL HELP

Finally, do not hesitate to call in your veterinary surgeon if difficulties are present that you cannot overcome. A womb may be twisted, a calf may be dead or bloated or for some other reason cannot be delivered.

SIGNS OF HEALTH

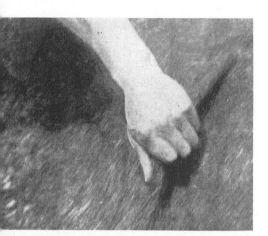

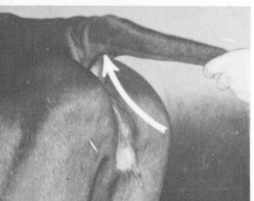

These pictures show, from top to bottom, signs of health to look for in a dairy cow—the bright and alert head and eyes with dewy muzzle; a loose silky skin; a pulse rate of 60 per minute (taken by applying index finger to roof of tail at point indicated); a temperature of 101-102° F, (38-40° C) taken per rectum. Bottom right-hand picture shows latest style veterinary thermometer with dial reading.

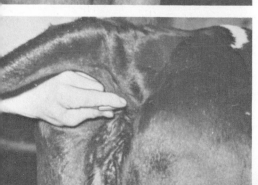

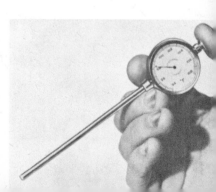

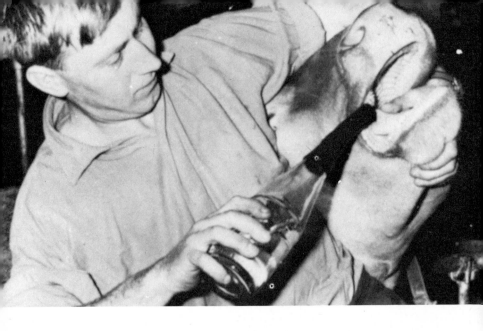

DRENCHING
A COW

Drenching can be carried out by push-button if one uses a sophisticated cattle drenching syringe such as that shown below. Most farmers, however, still resort to the use of a clean bottle. Photos show how to restrain the cow for dosing either unaided or with the help of an assistant. It is important to keep the animal's neck straight and to lower its head immediately if it coughs or chokes.
Note—the neck of the bottle is protected with an old teat liner.

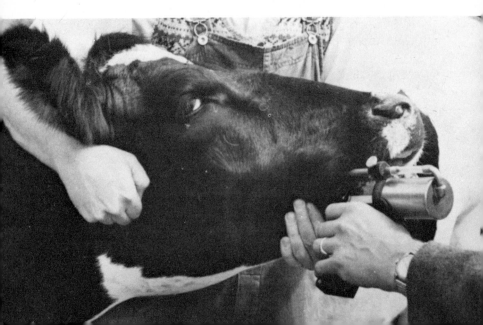

These tasks need professional knowledge.

In helping the cow and calf through their minor troubles and in calling assistance when required you are playing your part in the fight against disease in dairy herds.

It may be helpful to refer at this stage to the question of mummified calves which are often so difficult to explain and which often result in a calving date being passed without any sign of the cow starting to calve.

A mummified calf is due to a separation of the membranes uniting the calf to the cow and is usually the result of an injury during pregnancy. An hereditary factor – which is encountered more frequently in Channel Island breeds than any others – may sometimes be responsible.

The presence of a mummified calf is frequently associated with an extended period of gestation. The cow does not show the usual signs of approaching calving; indeed the time of calving passes and may be exceeded by weeks or even months before the somewhat reduced size of the cow makes one suspect a possible abortion.

DELAY MEANS LOSS

When an abnormal state like this is reached it is best to call in veterinary advice, preferably within two or three weeks of the due calving date. Otherwise, whilst the cow will remain alive, she will not come into season until the mummified calf is removed and, of course, will not come into milk until she calves again.

Even an expert may find it difficult to detect a mummified calf. Much of the fluid from its softer tissues will have been absorbed and it will lie well down in the extended womb. A hormone injection will probably be necessary to achieve its expulsion.

In view of my earlier remarks that mummified calves may be due to an hereditary factor you may question whether it is wise to retain a cow that produces a mummified calf. In general I think the best advice I can offer is to give a good cow one more chance; but do not serve her at her first normal season after veterinary attention – wait until the second. Conception is then more likely to occur.

As a final note on calving problems it may be well to mention here abnormalities such as bulldog calves in the Dexter breed and dropsical calves in Ayrshires.

The birth of a calf with these recognised characteristics – for example, with a face like a bulldog's or with an enormously swollen part or complete body – indicates that both the parents carried a recessive gene and that such parents should not be mated together again.

Other kinds of abnormal calves – for example with extra legs, twin heads, etc., can be regarded as freaks of nature which are unlikely to be repeated even if the same two parents are mated together again.

Abnormal calves are usually dead when born but if not they should, of course, be destroyed as quickly as possible. The best way is by knife directly into the heart or by cutting the throat with one clean sweep.

CHAPTER III

AFTER-CALVING TROUBLES

W E have discussed the problems that arise in preparing a cow for calving and helping her through that calving.

Now we can consider what should be done after calving to ensure that disease and difficulties are kept to a minimum.

The first problem you might meet immediately the calf has been delivered is when the navel cord does not rupture. If that happens simply cut the cord (with surgical scissors that have been boiled – not a dirty penknife!) about three or four inches (76 or 100 mm) from the calf.

This need only arises occasionally; normally you should be able to devote your attention, as soon as the calf has dropped to the ground, to stripping all the membranes from its body and particularly from its muzzle.

RISK OF SUFFOCATION

This is important. Calves are often lost from suffocation because their mouths and nostrils have been closed by a piece of afterbirth.

Then clean the nostrils and remove all mucus from the mouth.

Pull the tongue forward and make sure that the calf can breathe normally.

If it does not, you must take drastic measures.

There is no time for sentiment. Take a bucket of cold water and splash it over the calf's body. Slap its sides and ears, shout into its ears, and give it the kiss of life.

If that is not effective, it will be necessary to apply artificial respiration. With the calf lying on its side, grasp the shoulder

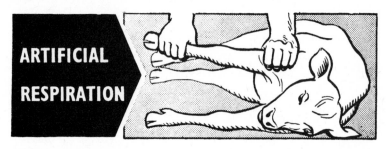

ARTIFICIAL
RESPIRATION

and lift the whole foreleg and shoulder up and down gently but firmly.

Once the calf is breathing you can attend to disinfecting the navel cord. First, tie it about an inch (25 mm) from the calf's body with a piece of thin string or tape that has been soaked in disinfectant. Then dust it thoroughly with sulphanilamide powder or paint it with iodine or Stockholm tar as a precaution against joint ill and scour infection.

Almost as soon as the calf has been dropped its mother will want to lick it dry. Let her do so. The rough action of her tongue will stimulate circulation in the calf and the licking will dry it.

In a straightforward calving without complications a vigorous calf will quickly struggle to its feet and within a short time will usually find its way to the teats and start sucking.

If the calf seems unable to find its way or the dam resents being sucked, then you should take steps to help the calf and, if necessary, control the cow with a halter, chain tie or leg strap.

WHEN CALF IS TAKEN FROM COW

Now just a word here to those who prefer to take the calf

from the cow immediately after calving – as is becoming more and more the practice in herds where an attempt is being made to control Johne's disease.

If you do this, see that the calf goes to a warm and well-strawed pen, that it is properly dried (a wisp of straw is the best thing to use) and that, as soon as it can suck, it gets some of its dam's colostrum at the proper temperature and from a sterilised vessel.

COLOSTRUM IS VITAL

This colostrum, the yellow and rather creamy liquid that takes the place of true milk for the first three or four days after calving, is vitally important to the calf for these reasons:

First, it is *laxative*, with a high fat content and encourages the expulsion of the first faecal material (meconium) from the calf.

Secondly, it is *protective*, owing to the presence of ready-made antibodies against certain ailments such as scour. During the first 24 hours of life these are absorbed through the intestinal wall.

Thirdly, it is *nutritive*, because it contains certain protein substances (phospho-casein) readily available to the calf.

Lastly, it is *fortifying*, through its high vitamin A content. (Here you will recall the advice previously given about feeding the cow with vitamin-rich foods before she calves. There is little or no vitamin A in a calf's liver when it is born.)

VALUE QUICKLY DECLINES

Now look at this table. It shows how the special qualities of colostrum decline from the moment lactation starts.

COMPARISON OF COLOSTRUM AND MILK

Time after calving	Total protein	Casein	Albumin and globulin	Sugar	Fat	Ash (Minerals)	Water
	%	%	%	%	%	%	%
*Immediately	17·57	5·08	11·34	2·19	5·10	1·01	73·01
*6 hours	10·00	3·51	6·30	2·71	6·85	0·91	79·54
*96 days	3·76	2·68	0·82	4·72	2·80	0·83	88·15
†Normal milk	3·42	2·86	0·56	4·78	3·67	0·73	86·00

*From "Chemistry of Milk" by W. D. Davies
†Average of figures from eight investigators.

37

It is against facts such as these that the practice of pre-milking and the different methods of calf rearing must be considered.

For example, what is a farmer to do for a new-born calf when its dam has been in milk, possibly for several days, before the calf was born or has died at calving?

SMALL AMOUNTS WILL DO

This is a vital matter because experiments have shown that the chances of a calf surviving are appreciably reduced if it does not get some colostrum within the first 36 hours of life. This appears to apply with greater emphasis to Jersey and Guernsey calves and to a lesser extent with Shorthorns and Ayrshires; Friesians seem to be the least affected by limited colostrum feeding.

On the other hand, it has been fairly well demonstrated that a calf needs only a small quantity of colostrum to gain the benefits of its protective and nutritive qualities and that, providing the dam has only been milked for a few days before calving, the milk she gives may in fact contain enough of those properties for the calf's well-being.

Thus the main problem is likely to occur when a cow has been in milk for a week or more before calving.

In such cases my advice is that you try to have available from another recently-calved cow some colostrum which you can give to the new calf for at least the first 24 hours of its life.

It is during those first 24 hours that the walls of the calf's bowel are sufficiently "porous" to let through into the blood stream the large globulin molecules in colostrum that carry the protective immunising properties.

STORING SURPLUS COLOSTRUM

One way of ensuring a supply of colostrum to meet exceptional cases is to store any surplus in the farmhouse refrigerator. This will keep it fresh for up to two weeks; for longer periods only deep-freeze is satisfactory.

The usual method of storing in deep-freeze is to use containers holding sufficient for one day's feed. Before feeding the colostrum is warmed up to body heat.

A "bank" of colostrum is particularly useful in cases where cows are purchased on the point of calving. By feeding their calves with colostrum from cows resident on the premises instead of with their dams' colostrum the appropriate disease antibodies will be supplied to the calves.

SUBSTITUTE FOR COLOSTRUM

Where no colostrum is available a useful substitute is one fresh egg whipped up in 1½ pints (852 ml) of milk to which is added half-a-pint (284 ml) of water, one teaspoonful of fresh cod-liver oil and up to one tablespoonful of castor oil with a half gram of streptomycin.

This should be given at blood heat in one feed.

(Newly-born calves can be given up to one tablespoonful of castor oil; after the first two days one teaspoonful is sufficient. During summer when cows are at grass there is no need to include cod-liver oil in the colostrum substitute.)

Now we come to the methods of feeding milk to a calf.

Here it must be remembered that a calf is not born ready-equipped to deal with any kind of food and to suffer any method of feeding. Its digestive system is delicate and specially adapted to use and digest milk. Later the system develops in such a way that it can deal more and more effectively with solid foods.

The drawings on page 41 will help to make the position clear.

The first shows that the rumen, the largest of the four stomachs in an older animal, is undeveloped at birth and is considerably smaller than the abomasum or true stomach. It is, in fact, not needed at this stage because the young calf does not eat coarse fodders that need to be broken down by bacteria in the process of rumination.

Thus it is "by-passed" by a groove that allows liquid (when properly fed) to pass directly into the abomasum where milk is digested. The inset picture, a cut-open view of the abomasum, shows this groove and the rumen opening clearly.

RISK OF FAULTY FEEDING

Let us see what happens if milk is fed too cold or too quickly. As the second sketch shows, most of the milk goes into the rumen which cannot deal with it. In that way faulty feeding can be the cause of digestive disorders.

Similarly, if milk is fed from buckets, then only part of it goes into the abomasum; some of it goes into the rumen where it is not required and may cause harm (see third sketch on page 41).

Later on the rumen develops as the last drawing shows and enables the calf to deal with coarser foods; but, in the early stages, the calf is only able to digest small feeds of milk preferably taken by sucking a cow or given through an artificial teat.

Remember these facts particularly, for the principles of calf feeding will arise again in the next chapter and this explanation will help you to understand the reasons behind them.

CARE OF COW AFTER CALVING

One trouble you may find is continued straining. You may be able to stop this by digging with the finger and thumb nails

PREVENTING STRAINING

on either side of the backbone; but if it persists, it may be necessary to tie a rope round the cow's belly. Leave it slack enough to insert a short stick in a loop of the rope and twist the stick to increase pressure as required.

Drenches of half-ounce (14 ml) doses of chlorodyne can be given every four hours as an additional help.

CALF'S DIGESTIVE SYSTEM

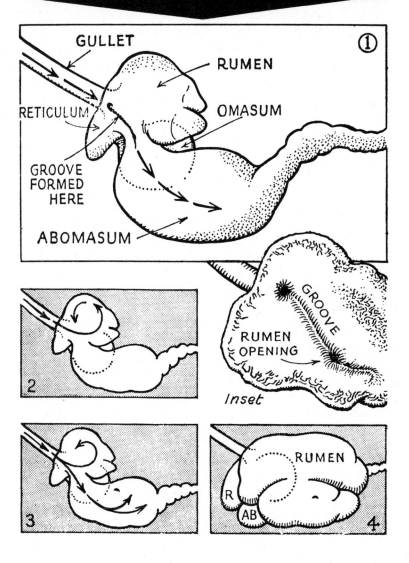

① GULLET
RUMEN
RETICULUM
OMASUM
GROOVE FORMED HERE
ABOMASUM

GROOVE
RUMEN OPENING
Inset

2

3

RUMEN
R
AB
4

Womb Eversion

It is wise to stop this straining as quickly as possible; if it is not checked it may lead to eversion of the womb.

Should that happen there are three things you must do: tie up the cow so that she cannot damage the womb; keep the womb as clean as possible; send for your vet.

Should the cow lie down, then soak a household sheet or tablecloth (something clean but not fluffy) in mild disinfectant and place it underneath the womb to protect it from dirt.

Veterinary attention is most essential. It is a skilled job to replace a womb; the organ is delicate and may be easily punctured or ruptured by rough manipulation.

If the cow has had an exhausting calving, then a stimulant is useful. One of the proprietary "cleansing" powders given in the recommended amount of warm water as a drench will be particularly suitable.

These drinks are stimulating and mildly purging. About one hour after, give 2 lb (907 g) of black treacle in 3 pints (1·70 l*) of warm water as an easily-assimilated food.

Even after a normal calving it is a good idea to offer the cow a warm bran mash, and you can continue to give such mashes twice daily for a few days. Not all cows will take them however.

During this critical period after calving see that the cow has a warm and dry bed and that she is protected from draughts.

BEST WAY TO GIVE DRENCH

I have just mentioned drenching; I shall be making continual references to it throughout this book, so a word or two about it might be helpful at this stage.

The important thing to watch in drenching an animal is that you do not let any liquid get into the windpipe or lungs – an event which would at least lead to choking and possibly to death from pneumonia. There is more danger of this when the drench contains oil than when it consists only of drugs in water.

The best procedure to follow is to get an assistant to stand by the left shoulder of the animal and to steady its head – by the horns if it has them; if not by encircling the head with his arm.

*l – litre

The person doing the drenching lifts up the animal's head just above horizontal and, at the same time, opens the mouth. This is done by standing on the right side, putting the left fore-arm over the animal's face and inserting four fingers in the dental space – between dental pad and corner of lip. The drenching bottle is then inserted in the right-hand side of the mouth.

Points to watch in drenching are:

1. Keep the beast's neck straight.
2. If the animal coughs or chokes let down nose immediately.
3. Use drenches cold, except where warm drenches are specifically stated.
4. See that irritant drugs are given well diluted or in gruel.
5. Never drench an animal with an obstruction in its gullet.
6. Never drench a semi-conscious animal, for example a case of milk fever.
7. Be very careful indeed if you have to drench one affected with lung trouble such as congestion or pneumonia or husk.

I have known cases of cut lips through bottles breaking when drenching. A good way to avoid this is to fit a short piece of rubber hose or an old teat cup liner onto the drenching bottle. This has the further advantage of allowing liquids to be placed well back in the mouth – and that makes for easier swallowing.

But don't take too long over drenching, otherwise the cow will start to chew the rubber.

Some farmers and herdsmen consider it wise to withhold drinking water from a cow before and after drenching. There is little point in this, although some of the drench will pass directly into a cow's fourth stomach if she is thirsty.

After-Calving Paralysis (*The Recumbent Cow*)

To return to other after-calving problems.

First I should mention paralysis – *post-parturient paralysis* – a condition that all too often occurs after calving. Some cases may be due to pressure during calving on the nerves inside the pelvis, making it impossible for the cow to use her hind legs.

These are splayed out and the animal is unable to rise despite frantic efforts.

There is really little you can do, although you can give an Epsom salts drench – 1 lb (454 g) in a pint (570 ml) of cold water – and nerve tonic drenches that your vet will supply. You can also rub the back behind the ribs with liniment and cover with a sack.

Keep the cow propped up on her brisket with straw bales. Placing a tarpaulin over the bedding and under the cow is ideal. Such a procedure will avoid bed sores and prevent the limbs from becoming cramped.

Modern knowledge of cortisone-like substances may help in producing a cure, and your vet may perhaps wish to try one of these, or to inject a mixture of calcium and phosphorus and probably magnesium. This sometimes helps. It has also been noted that on occasion an electric goad applied to the buttock produces a miracle, but the main factors are generally time and rest.

However, experience has taught us that if such an affected cow is not up by the tenth day, it is best to have her slaughtered. Rare cases have been known to recover after a longer period, but the complications of bed sores and emaciation involve attention for a long time.

HOW SOON TO MILK OUT?

It is now becoming a generally accepted practice not to milk a cow right out for at least 24 hours after calving. Wait for 48 hours if you can, just letting the calf take what it requires during this time and easing any quarter that the calf may not touch.

This practice should apply whether the cow was milked before calving or not.

If the calf was taken away at birth, then draw from the cow just enough to feed the calf, taking an equal amount from each quarter. Do the same if the calf dies.

This is a safeguard against milk fever which will be dealt with fully in a subsequent chapter.

OFFERING COLOSTRUM TO COW

Some farmers make a practice of offering surplus colostrum to the cow when she is first milked. Not all cows will take it, but if they will it is certainly beneficial to them.

However, I would prefer to use any surplus colostrum for calves. Those that are on an ordinary diet will benefit from a feed of colostrum instead of one of their normal milk feeds. It may cause them to scour a little but it will do them good.

Alternatively, of course, surplus colostrum can be "banked" in a refrigerator or deep-freeze for future calves.

Blood in Milk

Just one more point about the milk from a freshly-calved cow.

You may find it tinted with blood to a greater or lesser degree. This is caused when some of the small blood vessels in the udder break down under the strain and release blood into the milk-producing system.

It is usually nothing to worry about. Milk the cow carefully, avoiding any vigorous action, and do not strip out entirely for a day or two. The milk will quickly become normal.

The injection of vitamin K sometimes gives good results.

Retained Afterbirth

Now we come to the problem of retained afterbirth.

This afterbirth, or cleansing, is the "bag" in which the calf developed. On the outer surface of this membraneous bag there are a hundred or more cotyledons which are attached to corresponding cotyledons or "buttons" on the wall of the womb.

Normally, immediately after calving, the womb begins to contract and squeeze out the cleansing and any fluid left behind. The afterbirth may be discharged within a short time, in which case all should be well. But don't let the cow eat the afterbirth, it may choke her.

If it remains completely inside the cow or hangs unpleasantly from her, it may be necessary to help with its removal.

The first step is to insert daily a pessary of chinosol or gentian violet or one of the standard preparations. Gently, with hand and forearm thoroughly clean and well-lubricated with disinfectant oils or soap, work the pessary alongside the afterbirth, about 8 or 10 inches (200 or 250 mm) into the passage or into the mouth of the womb if this is still open.

An afterbirth may hang for four days in winter or for three days in summer in the case of a cow; one day less for a heifer. If it goes beyond these periods you should call in professional assistance rather than attempt its removal yourself. A detailed knowledge of anatomy is required to perform this operation without causing haemorrhage and penetration.

But nowadays injection by your vet of the appropriate hormone may be all that is necessary.

DANGER OF WASHING-OUT WOMB

Should an afterbirth hang from the cow and drag the floor, cut off all that is below the hocks. Don't hang bricks or sticks on it as they may get caught up and cause it to tear away too soon. If, however, there is a herd problem, then an intramuscular injection of 15 mg of potassium selenate and 700 i.u. of vitamin E is to be recommended. This is effective for up to four weeks.

Don't use any fluid to wash out the womb. Fluids have the effect of distending the womb at a time when it should start to contract; further, when a fluid has been used it can only be removed by syphoning – which is not always successful.

Stick to the pessaries as the best safeguard against infection and regard exercise and good feeding as the most sensible and effective farm treatment in any case of retained afterbirth.

Retained afterbirths are not always due to infection; they can be caused by a shortage of the right sort of protein in the steaming-up ration. Iodine and vitamin E may also play a part.

VALUE OF PROTEIN

Ensure that the steaming-up ration contains from 5 to 7 per cent of a good quality animal protein (fishmeal, meat and bone meal, etc.) and an iodised mineral supplement. An alternative way of providing the iodine is to use iodised mineral licks.

Where there are signs that retained afterbirths are a herd problem – i.e. when many cows in the herd have this trouble – the possibility of an iodine deficiency should not be overlooked, particularly if the herd is fed on large quantities of kale.

For reasons as yet unknown kale, in some years only, contains a goitrogenic factor which interferes with the cows' iodine intake.

Where this is suspected as a possible cause of retained afterbirths, it might be worth trying a few cows with a course of wooden tongue drenches (these contain iodine) before calving or giving each cow 50 grains (3 g) of potassium iodide daily for about a week, again just before calving (see also under Production Diseases).

Puerpural Metritis

There is one other disease to mention at this stage. It is puerpural metritis, an inflammation of the womb from which poisons may get into the blood stream. It occurs from 2 to 5 days after calving and arises from an infection, possibly due to failure to cleanse properly or to tears in the wall of the womb.

Perhaps the only indication you will notice is that the cow goes off her food. She will probably have a temperature. Sometimes there may be straining, staggering, and scouring. These are signs you should not ignore, for the cow may die if neglected. Injections and the use of sulpha drugs and antibiotics by your veterinary surgeon will usually effect a cure.

Fortunately, this trouble is one likely to occur in isolated cases. On the whole the womb of a cow is remarkably resistant to infection and stands up well to hard usage during a difficult calving.

Indeed, given good management and no infective conditions, your freshly-calved cow will have every chance of avoiding the many possible complications and should be fit to return to the herd four or five days after the event.

Just when you turn her out is a matter for personal discretion, partly influenced by the weather. The only point I make is that you satisfy yourself that all after-calving discharge from the womb has ceased before she mixes with other cows.

CAUTION WITH CONCENTRATES

Lastly, be somewhat cautious in starting to feed concentrates. If they are given too suddenly after calving or fed in over-large amounts at first there is a grave risk of indigestion.

Begin with 2 lb (907 g) night and morning on second or the third day after calving and increase by not more than 2 lb (907 g) a day until you are giving the full production ration by about the tenth day.

If it is your normal practice to feed a little above the production ration to encourage an increasing yield, I suggest you do not start this until the second or third week after calving.

Displaced Abomasum

This condition is included because the symptoms frequently resemble those of acetonaemia. It is possible that many cases have been diagnosed as the latter, and because they have in fact been associated with the displacement of this organ, response to standard treatment has not been all that might have been expected.

The abomasum is the true or fourth stomach and lies on the floor of the abdomen. The abnormality is by no means a new phenomenon but has probably gone under the guise of other conditions in the past, *i.e.* the above.

As in acetonaemia there is generally a history of recent parturition, and unless specially investigated this displacement is unlikely to come to light. Its importance largely lies in the fact that it can be mistaken for, or masked by, symptoms of acetonaemia or general indigestion. There are seldom any distinct lesions at post-mortem. In fact, its displacement is unlikely to be recognised without the greatest of care being taken. Since 1950 reports of this occurrence have been increasing. There is a tendency for its displacement to the left in any case during pregnancy and parturition, but displacement may be exaggerated, and when there is a readjustment of pressures after parturition it may be trapped. This, however, is not thought to be the sole cause, many cases probably being initiated by a lack of tone in the organ, resulting in the accumulation of gas and a further tendency for displacement into the left flank. The greatly increased consumption of concentrates and a low roughage intake following calving could well be important in controlling the consistency of the abomasal contents. More hay may well help.

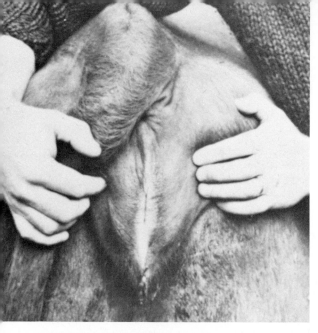

SIGNS OF CALVING

As calving time approaches the vulva will become grossly enlarged. The lips will part slightly, the inner tissue becomes pinker and there will be a discharge of clear mucus.

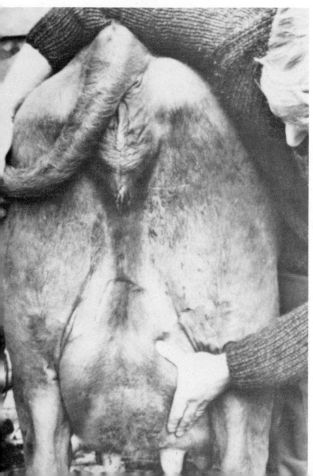

Twelve hours before calving the udder will be fully distended and pressure with the fingers will leave deep impressions. The teats will also stiffen.

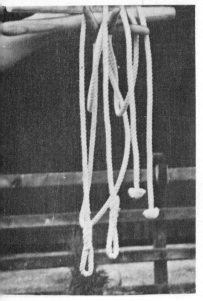

CALVING DOWN
A COW

Top pictures show the beginning of normal-presentation calving, with calf's head between forelegs. Lower picture shows the tackle required when assistance is given—nylon ropes with handles to facilitate pulling.

Ropes should be fixed above the calf's fetlocks; traction should be downward as shown in top right picture. Once the calf is delivered the cow should do the rest—see right-hand picture.

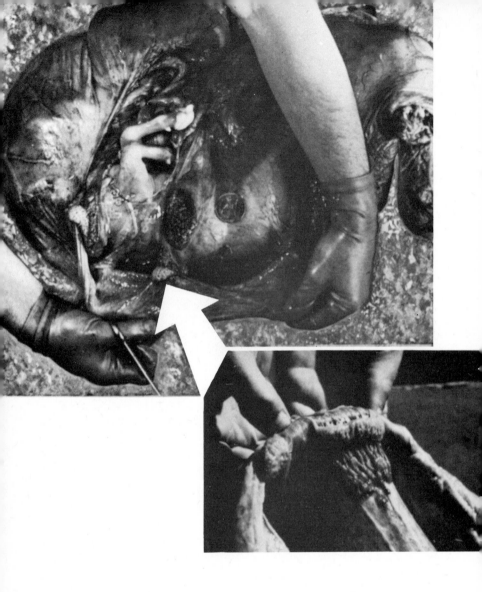

Top picture shows womb lining cut away to reveal calf and
cotyledon attachments—rather larger than the old penny in
the picture.

Below: A close up of the cotyledon attachment which shows
how adhesion between calf membranes and uterus lining is
achieved.

CHAPTER IV

TREATMENT OF BABY CALF DISEASES

HAVING dealt with the problems likely to arise with the cow during the first few days after calving, we will now turn to the calf and see what we can do for the first three or four weeks of its life to avoid the troubles that so frequently occur.

It is probably your practice to take the calf from its dam at about the fourth day after calving. So let us first deal with housing the calf.

There is one good rule to apply here. It is: beware of draughts.

They are no good to any animal, least of all a young one. And the worst draught of all is a down-draught.

By all means see that calves get fresh air, but not an arctic blast. Chilling will seriously reduce their resistance to disease.

IMPORTANCE OF VENTILATION

If you have a properly designed calf-pen it will have a low roof and correct ventilation that assures regular changing of air in the building without creating a draught.

If you use a converted barn or stable and the roof is more than

PLANS FOR CALF HOUSES

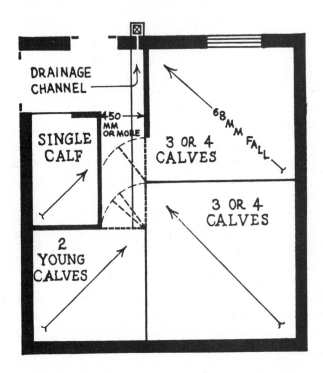

DRAINAGE CHANNEL

450 MM OR MORE

SINGLE CALF

3 OR 4 CALVES

68 MM FALL

3 OR 4 CALVES

2 YOUNG CALVES

This plan shows useful way of converting loose box or stable to calf house. For single calves minimum size of pen should be 20 ft. (6·10 m). Older calves in groups require at least 40 sq. ft. (3.72² m) each.

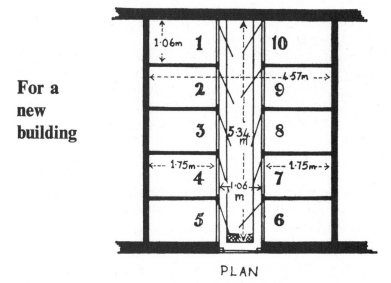

PLAN

For a new building

Plan above shows suitable layout for individual pen calf house. With hopper-type windows (6 sq. ft. (0·557 m²) of window space per calf), with lined roof and adjustable air extractor, conditions should be the best possible for calves. Detail below is of floor and partition construction. Solid partitions prevent draughts; tubular gates enable calves to see their neighbours.

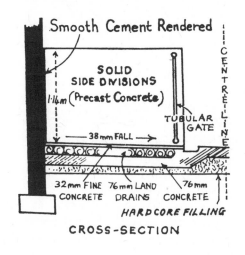

CROSS-SECTION

Build it yourself details

14 feet (4·77 m) high then it is a good plan to make a false ceiling at a height of about 6 feet (1·83 m) with some spars or hurdles or wire netting and cover it with a layer of two or three inches (50 or 76 mm) of straw.

Fresh air can be obtained in many ways. Perhaps the best is to use hopper-type windows. Foul air should be discharged, preferably through a controlled ridge ventilation system or chimney. Where natural air-flow is difficult owing to, say, the proximity of other buildings, extractor fans may be necessary.

INSULATING FLOORS

Make a point, too, of having the floor concreted and the walls cement-rendered up to about 3 ft. 6 in. (1·06 m) so that thorough disinfection can be practised. And when laying the concrete floor insulate it to make it less cold. An air space below the surface

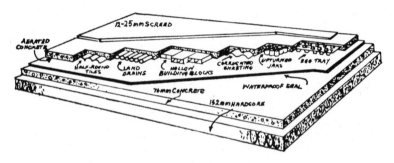

Cheap and effective floor insulation.

is the best means. This can be obtained by using land tiles, air bricks, bottles or other materials below the surface concrete. A layer of roofing felt on top of the hardcore base is a further safeguard against rising damp.

A PEN FOR EACH CALF

My final advice on housing is to divide your calf premises so that each calf has a separate pen with solid walls in preference to open-sided or tubular partitions. There is no better way than this of avoiding serious trouble from an infectious disease which

PRINCIPLES OF CALF-HOUSE VENTILATION

This will get cold and damp

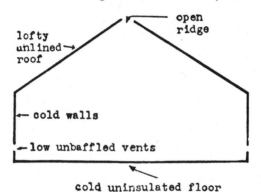

This will keep warm and dry

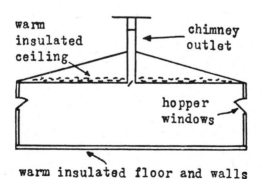

may otherwise sweep quickly through a large bunch of calves herded together in a restricted space.

If you prefer to keep your calves in groups then limit each group to three or four calves.

OUTDOOR REARING

With the trend towards more extensive methods of stock management, the idea of keeping spring and early summer calves in movable outdoor houses or tethering them near straw bale shelters is well worth considering.

Such a dispersal reduces risk of spreading infectious scours and lung diseases.

ADVICE ON FEEDING

And now to feeding. Here again I must emphasise the importance of colostrum in protecting the calf from bacterial invasion and the need for care in feeding the dam suitably (*e.g.* with good quality green hay if she is not out at grass), during her dry period so that her colostrum is of the highest quality.

If the dam is moved to new premises before she calves the antibodies in her colostrum may not protect her calf against the fresh organisms to which it is exposed on the new premises. So the beneficial effect of colostrum is thus weakened. It is best that in-calf heifers or cows be exposed for at least six weeks to the new premises to ensure a reasonable build-up of protection.

Once the calf leaves its dam it is usually bucket-fed. If so, bear in mind the facts I gave earlier about the young calf's digestive system.

Bear in mind, too, that with normal digestion in the abomasum or fourth stomach, the milk is there formed into a clot before it is broken down prior to digestion by enzymes. The type of clot varies with the quantity and quality of milk fed; if a large quantity is given at one feed, then a large clot is formed.

This will take some time to digest and if it is not completely digested before the next feed is given, then a nucleus remains round which the next clot may be formed.

If this process continues, a tough, hard mass is built up which may interfere with the calf's well-being. This is a form of indigestion that may have an indirect action on the brain and cause staggering or fits, or it may be a prelude to white scour.

Calves are tough little animals but a certain routine is desirable. A good system is to allow them to suckle their dams for 12 hours after birth. It is essential they get colostrum soon after they are born since the intestine will only allow the preformed antibodies to pass through its walls for about the first 24 hours. Afterwards the calves are then individually penned and bucket-fed for three days with warm colostrum (that from another cow or a deep-freeze bank will be quite satisfactory). The antibodies circulating in the bowel may well help to reduce the onset of scouring. On the fourth day the calves are switched to a single daily feed of 1 lb (454 g) of milk substitute mixed with 6 pints (3·40 l) of warm water. Some calves may have to be finger-fed to persuade them to accept the change.

EARLY WEANING

The method of early weaning is now well established and has proved to have many advantages. Once the routine has been mastered it is simple and labour saving, the incidence of scours tends to be less, and milk is saved for the liquid market. A calf is not a ruminant animal when born. It is a milk-drinker. Hence the relatively greater size of the abomasum or true stomach as compared with the other stomachs. Rumination depends on the full development of the ruminal lining, a process brought about by offering solid food at about the fourth day. This contains high-quality protein and fatty acids which stimulate the growth of the ruminal lining. A small quantity of good hay is offered to avoid digestive troubles but too much will delay the process of development we're encouraging. By five to six weeks most animals will be able to deal with solid food alone.

So long as the method is correctly applied, there is little

difference in weight at the age of three months between calves reared on whole milk and those by the early-weaning method, though the latter may well look rather rougher.

Although the method can be applied to both beef and dairy calves, it would appear to be unwise to force the latter too much. They will come into season too early and milk yields subsequently are depressed.

White Scour

White scour is, in fact, the most troublesome of calf diseases.

Here it is well to say at the outset that, although chills and indigestion are predisposing factors to scour, most cases are in fact due to infection of the dreaded "white scour" type that attacks calves during the first few weeks of their life.

The gut of the new-born calf is such that it is completely free from bacteria when it is born. But immediately following the first feed bacteria can be found in plenty. Subsequently the bowel, like that of any other animal, contains vast numbers of bacteria – including coliform organisms. These have a natural function to perform. But there are some strains of coliform organisms that are responsible for infectious "scour".

Some of these strains are mild in their attack; others are virulent. The virulent ones may get the upper hand with any calf, even though it is properly fed and managed. The weaker ones may be present in the calf's bowel and cause no harm – unless bad feeding or exposure to chills so weaken the calf that the germs get the upper hand.

Sometimes they do so with such speed that the calf dies before any signs of scour can appear; sometimes they cause not only scouring but pneumonia; sometimes, by a kind of delayed action, they cause joint-ill.

THE SYMPTOMS

Scour from this cause can develop within a few hours or a few days of birth but most frequently arises during the first two weeks of life. The symptoms in the early stages are that the calf will appear dull and will suck listlessly or may refuse to suck altogether. Its appearance may be very dejected.

A prominent symptom is greyish white diarrhoea with possibly an increase in temperature at first which may later become sub-normal. There is usually a characteristic sweet and pleasant odour associated with the condition at this stage; but it quickly changes to sourness.

The calf rapidly gets weaker and becomes unable to stand; its eyes become sunken. Unless remedial action is taken and is successful it will die.

This trouble is most frequently met with in winter, especially the latter end of winter – February to April. It occurs much less frequently in summer.

Salmonella Scours

Whilst most cases are associated with coliform organisms some may be due to infection with a bacterium of the salmonella group (usually *S. dublin* type). The presence of blood in the droppings is a useful means of differentiating this form of scour from the more common coliform type – but it is not always present.

RISK WITH PURCHASED CALVES

There are several matters of extreme importance here. A change of premises constitutes a stress and transport only exaggerates this. So it is best not to move calves until they are at least ten days old. If they are then to be moved they should be taken direct to the farm where they are going to live and not go via a collecting centre.

At five days they should be vaccinated with a salmonella vaccine (Mellavax). Immunity will rapidly build up so that at the end of a week the calves could be moved. If scouring should appear after vaccination on no account use an antibiotic since this will nullify the good effects of the vaccine immediately.

Even if the herd is self-contained a strong case can be made out for vaccinating the calves since salmonellosis is very much on the increase and the risks of it appearing are very much greater than a few years ago. Calves and cows can be carriers of infection without any indication and should there be a breakdown due to some environmental disturbance then the salmonella organisms may become active and the infection could spread to the adult herd. This can be very serious indeed. So you should consult your veterinary surgeon to decide upon a policy of vaccination and also a system of procedure should scouring occur.

If conditions are unsatisfactory, successive cases of salmonellosis tend to increase in virulence and to spread rapidly to healthy calves. Once established on the farm the disease is difficult to get rid of as the organisms persist in the woodwork of old buildings, in bedding and dried-up dung.

Newly-purchased, susceptible animals brought in from another farm or a market, may well become infected themselves and start a virulent outbreak or, if the disease is already active, become ready victims and help to increase the virulence and infectivity of the organisms.

This is a very strong reason for isolating all bought-in young stock until they have become accustomed to their new environment or until the termination of any current outbreak.

All this means that the first need on the farm to combat this disease is strict attention to cleanliness.

That is why I advised calving down in a loose box that is cleaned out regularly and well littered and that can be thoroughly disinfected after each calving.

Similar precautions should be taken in the calf pens. This is easier if the pens have solid partitions as already recommended.

Yet another factor is the use of dirty feeding utensils. They should be kept scrupulously clean and steam-sterilised or scalded at least once a day.

Apart from paying the most careful attention to disinfection you should ensure a good, warm, dry environment and a proper diet, properly fed.

I have already referred to the value of colostrum in this respect and to the rules for feeding it. Everything should be done to avoid digestive upsets, particularly when changing over from whole milk to milk substitutes.

SCOUR PREVENTION AND CONTROL

If you are in doubt as to whether the calves you have bought have received colostrum there is a simple test which can be carried out, and which you could do yourself after instruction. As the colostrum may be deficient in the right sort of antibodies and because very young animals take time to build up their own immunity a valuable procedure is to inject gamma globulin (of which there are a number of preparations on the market) into the bloodstream. This is the serum fraction of the blood which carries the antibodies. In an emergency a blood transfusion from the dam to the calf is worth while – taking the blood from the jugular vein of the cow and injecting it directly into the muscles of the calf. Or, more scientifically, remove 500 ml into a vessel containing an anti-coagulant, shake gently and inject half under the skin on each side of the calf. This process has been further refined and plasma drip infusion is now possible. Bottles of plasma are available and can be fixed above the calf and connected to the calf's jugular vein, the animal's movements being restricted during the process.

ROUTINE PRECAUTIONS

But the treatment to be adopted depends largely on the nature of the case. For example, special drugs can now be employed where salmonella organisms are involved.

So a proper diagnosis is clearly an advantage – which is one simple reason why it pays to leave matters in the hands of a veterinary surgeon.

Nevertheless, upon an outbreak of scour you are advised to take these routine precautions:

1. Isolate the calves, keep them dry and keep them warm by using an infra-red lamp or by rugging them with sacks.
2. If whole milk is being fed dilute this four times and feed half the total volume, spreading this over the 24-hour period and feeding at four-hourly intervals.
3. Another method is to alternate the milk feeding by drenching with eight pints (4·55 l) of the following mixture: 1 teaspoonful salt, $\frac{1}{2}$ teaspoonful sodium

bicarbonate, 4 ounces (113 g) glucose, 4 pints (2·27 l) water plus antibiotics. The latter, of course, will not be included if you are treating a case of salmonellosis. The scouring calf rapidly becomes dehydrated losing fluids and failing to absorb any nutrients. It is thus a bad thing to cut off its milk and give it simply glucose and water at this stage, for this merely encourages the loss of valuable salts. Beneficial effects are reported by the injection of certain substances into the peritoneal cavity. Good results have also been reported from the injection of 100 cc of 5 per cent salt solution. Alternatively, the following solution can be injected under the skin – 1 ounce (28 g) glucose, 1 dram (17 mg) common salt, 0·25 grains acriflavine, 16 ounces (454 g) water. The ingredients can be made up separately, ready to add to water at body temperature when required.

Clostridium welchii Infection

The same germs that are found in the sheep's bowel are to be found in that of the calf, but they seldom cause any trouble. Four types, namely B, C, D, and E, have been identified.

Occasionally a few animals are involved in a severe attack showing signs of acute enteritis, but it is not known what precipitates these. There is acute haemorrhagic inflamation affecting the upper small bowel with unaltered blood present at postmortem. The local lymph glands and the heart are involved suggesting the presence of a toxin. There is no ulceration. Death is often sudden without symptoms.

If a number of cases occur then it may be worthwhile considering the use of a mixed vaccine.

Navel-Ill or Joint-Ill

This is due to bacteria that, in most cases, gain access to the calf when the navel cord is not properly treated at birth. Not all farms have this infection but,where it occurs, serious losses can be sustained.

In acute cases death is rapid and there may be no specific symptoms except that the calf groans and grunts and is obviously ill. Only a post-mortem can then prove the cause.

In less acute cases the disease is characterised by swollen and painful joints, the hocks and knees being most commonly affected. Sometimes there is a swelling of the navel and an abscess may be formed there.

Hot fomentations applied to affected parts every four hours may help. When buying in calves of a few days old, the navel should be carefully inspected.

FARM TREATMENT

On the farm you cannot do more to prevent this disease than to make sure you treat the navel cord at birth and that you observe strictly the rules already given – both with regard to cleanliness and to feeding – for preventing scour. The reason for this is that navel-ill and scouring are closely associated.

Lead Poisoning

If fits or convulsions occur you should be highly suspicious of lead poisoning. Many calves die every year from this because insufficient care is taken to ensure that they cannot lick paint-work. They often appear to be blind.

This is important, particularly in old buildings where paint may be flaking. Doors and walls are usually responsible, but even ceilings may be shedding flakes that the calves are likely to pick up.

Make sure that this risk is avoided. Scrape all old paintwork thoroughly, and do not even temporarily put calves into buildings where paint is peeling off. Doors are better covered with zinc or aluminium or asbestos-cement sheets.

Remember, too, that new paint can be equally dangerous. If you wish to use paint, then choose one with a zinc base that will do no harm. Alternatively you could use creosote on previously unpainted wood.

The natural inquisitiveness of calves when out of doors may result in fatalities if they have access to old tins of paint or materials such as tarpaulins, old coach work, etc., treated with lead-containing preparations.

Should a case of suspected lead poisoning arise, you must act quickly. Give immediately, as a drench, half-a-dozen raw eggs whisked up in a jug. If these are not readily available a drench of $\frac{1}{2}$ ounce (14 g) of Epsom salts in half a pint (284 ml) of water should be given and repeated three or four times at half-hourly intervals.

Stomach Staggers (Magnesium Deficiency)

Lead poisoning is not to be confused with stomach staggers which is now thought to be due to a lack of magnesium in the diet.

It has been shown that this is a fairly common condition in beef calves fed for a prolonged period on milk alone. The latter provides insufficient magnesium with the result that their reserves run out and they show signs of marked excitement, alarm, staggering, and inco-ordination.

This is a condition comparable to grass staggers in adult cattle, although it appears to be a pure deficiency, whereas the latter, although associated with the fall in blood magnesium, is induced by environmental conditions and is not a simple deficiency. The remedy is simple – a tablespoonful of milk of magnesia daily in the milk for three days, commencing immediately the first signs occur.

When two or three animals are affected all the rest of the group should receive the same treatment and steps should be taken, in consultation with the veterinary surgeon, to provide a suitable mineral supplement in order to prevent a recurrence.

The condition may be precipitated by stimulating and causing excitement such as chasing them round the box, an injection, the presence of a stranger, or even just bringing them their normal meals.

Hairballs in Stomach

Sometimes hairballs, often formed by animals licking their skins to allay irritation due to lice, are formed in the stomach and give rise to fits or convulsions. Similarly, pieces of binder twine and sacking and other foreign bodies may be responsible. Even straw will form a mat in the stomach and that, too, is sometimes thought to be a cause of fits and death.

It is not easy to distinguish between fits due to lead poisoning and to binder twine, etc., though in the former instance several animals are generally affected together. There may be champing of the jaws and frothing, convulsions and kicking. The calves' sight is usually impaired; they will run blindly round the box and may attempt to climb the wall.

Where binder twine is the cause the animals may become dull and sleepy between fits.

A pint (57 ml) of thick cornflour or ground oatmeal gruel may help along a piece of twine, though cases are often fatal.

Now you cannot stop calves from licking themselves, but you can make allowances for the fact that they are inquisitive beggars and see that binder twine is not left in the bedding and that odd pieces of sacking are not within the calves' reach.

To prevent them from eating straw it is best to see that, quite early in their life, a supply of really good, fragrant and soft hay is put in front of them. It's surprising how soon a calf will begin to take an interest in solid food, and some of the best hay in nets or racks (not on the floor) will prove more attractive than bedding.

Muzzle any calf with a depraved appetite and treat any skin condition which may be causing undue irritation.

Lastly, even if you are not able to provide individual pens for your calves, do try and give them individual feeding by tying them up at meal time. If they have to compete for food, particularly for milk, they will gulp it down. And that may lead to some of the very troubles which we are trying to avoid.

PREVENT CROSS-SUCKLING

Further, individual feeding in this way can be a means of preventing cross-suckling. Leave the calves tied up for half an hour or so after their milk feed and while they eat their concentrates. Before you release them wipe their muzzles thoroughly dry and they will then have no desire to suck

This may be more important than you think. It is possible that summer mastitis germs get into the animal through a tooth-scratched teat, in young life.

Take tablespoonful cornflour or ground oatmeal, mix to paste with cold water, add boiling water to make up to one pint (57 ml), stir and cool quickly.

Vitamin A Deficiency

Calves sometimes suffer from deficiencies of vitamins, in particular A and D. (Shortages of B and C are unlikely because ruminant animals produce their own supplies.)

Vitamin A deficiency may be caused by a lack of this vitamin in the milk of the dam and result in general unthriftiness, some-times associated with scouring. Vision becomes less sensitive – especially in dull light – and may be suspected when animals bump into things at dusk or in shady or dark pens. Skin becomes scurfy and staring.

A condition of blindness, especially in Channel Island breeds but also encountered in other breeds to a lesser extent, is occasionally noticed and is thought to be hereditary.

It is possible that the conformation of the skull is affected by nutritional deficiencies or variations in early life resulting in malformation of the bones and pressure on and stretching of the nerves to the eyes.

Where the condition exists at birth, calves adapt themselves so well to their surroundings that such a defect may not be observed until they are removed to a strange environment. Then they will bump into things, stand with their heads up and their ears alert, and can be approached and touched before they will move.

Another condition associated with a cataract is sometimes

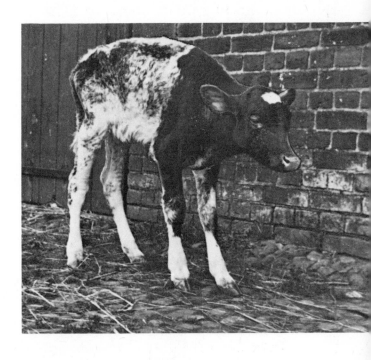

Above: A typical case of a calf affected with white scour—hunched back, sunken ribs, dejected appearance. *Below:* Lungs from a calf infected with husk.

In this controlled-environment calf-house the animals are individually housed in slatted-timber pens which can be removed between batches for thorough cleaning of the building. Note the provision of individual buckets for both feed and water.

A clean, bright and airy calf-house that provides individual penning by means of metal mesh divisions but is free from draughts. Each calf has access to hay, water and feed, the water and feed buckets being easily detached for cleaning. But respiratory diseases could spread easily.

An arrangement gaining in popularity in New Zealand is where the calves are at grass during summer but ushered back into wire-mesh pens for feeding. Design features here are the herringbone stalls and the metal 'gates' preventing calves from feeding until all are in position and the 'gates' opened mechanically by the stockman. (Photo: Charters & Guthie, New Plymouth).

TAKE
CARE
OF
YOUR
CALVES

With labour becoming harder to obtain and more expensive to provide, many dairy farmers are using mechanical feeders for the rearing of large groups of calves. The model shown here automatically mixes the milk replacer and water in the correct proportions, heats it to the right temperature and cuts off the supply to the teat when the calf has taken its ration.

These calves are housed in solid partition cubicles and their feed dispensed into individual buckets from a 'robot' feeder running on a track at the front of the pens.

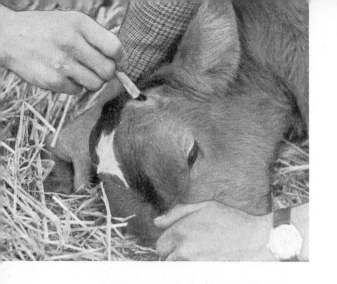

THREE WAYS
TO DISBUD
CALVES

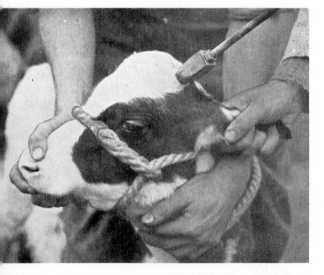

Top picture shows application of a dehorning collodion applied by stiff brush which is supplied with the collodion sold by veterinary chemists. Centre picture illustrates the hot-iron method. Lower picture is of an electric cauteriser. The use of hot irons and electric cauterisers is now illegal unless the calf has first been effectively anæsthetized.

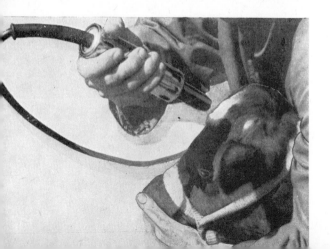

encountered and is of unknown origin. It may be confused with that due to vitamin A.

Vitamin D Deficiency

A vitamin D deficiency may also result when there is a lack of this in the milk and when calves are kept indoors. Their coats become staring; they become pot-bellied and fail to grow. Rickets may appear, the joints becoming swollen and the legs – especially the lower parts – tending to bend under the weight of the body.

A condition of rickets may occur if there is an excess of calcium or a deficiency of phosphorus in the diet though this state of affairs is more likely to be encountered in calves of about three or four months than of a few weeks.

Vitamin deficiencies should never occur when feeding and management are good. If they do, they can quickly be brought under control, so long as the symptoms have not existed too long, by feeding of small quantities of fresh cod-liver oil which contains vitamins A and D. You should see that the ration is not rancid (stored too long in a hot place) and that it does in fact contain the necessary amounts of the vitamins in question.

An initial dose of $\frac{1}{4}$ pint (142 ml) of cod-liver oil to a three-month-old calf will be found satisfactory.

It is also possible to feed synthetic preparations of both these vitamins (or to give injections of them) and so build up the body's reserves very rapidly.

A point to be borne in mind when using cod-liver oil is that it may lose its vitamin potency if it is exposed to light and air. It should accordingly be stored in a cool dark place, and the container should never be left unstopped. Small and frequent purchases are safer than buying in large amounts.

When cod-liver oil or other fish oils are exposed to light and air they become oxidised and may then contain harmful fatty acids. There now seems little doubt that feeding such defective oil destroys the vitamin E in the ration with the result that calves may well develop muscular dystrophy.

Such a risk will be avoided by the injection of synthetic vitamins or by feeding them in dry specialised form either added to the minerals or sprinkled on the food.

Vitamin E Deficiency (White Muscle Disease)

Vitamin E deficiency is very clearly responsible for a condition known as muscular dystrophy occurring in beef calves reared on cows which have been fed on nothing but straw and beet pulp.

The cow's vitamin E reserves are depleted on this ration so that she has none available to pass to her calf – with the result that the muscle tissue is seriously affected. This not only applies to the muscles of the body but to the heart which is almost entirely specialised muscle tissue. At post-mortem white streaks may often be observed on the heart and a herringbone pattern on certain muscles.

The storage of wet grain treated with an anti-fungal agent, such as propionic acid, has introduced a new problem, for such a procedure can deplete the vitamin E content within a few weeks. Therefore, as soon as young stock are put on a high grain diet, also *deficient in selenium*, they become susceptible. Symptoms often appear when stock are turned out after over-wintering in doors and exposed to the stresses of inclement weather, sudden exercise, etc. There is marked respiratory distress and inco-ordination of movement. A ration fortified with 3-4 ppm of selenium is thought to be beneficial in these circumstances.

SYMPTOMS TO LOOK FOR

The symptoms of muscular dystrophy are very varied. Any excitement such as the arrival of a stranger or the clatter of buckets may increase sensitivity, causing the animal to stagger around. Transport of animals by sea may also have adverse effects and treatment with vitamin E and selenium appears to be effective. In other cases there is stiffness of the fore limbs, with knuckling over of the fetlocks, the calf finding it difficult to get up and walk about. It carries its fore limbs forwards and outwards and takes slow steps.

The chest is often dropped so that the line of the backbone

falls below the shoulder blades and the points of the pelvic girdle. The points of the shoulders may protrude outwards, causing a large hollow between the neck and the scapula into which the fist will readily go. The muscles are painful.

If the chest muscles are affected, breathing tends to be difficult and to be largely abdominal in nature. If the diaphragm is affected there may be exaggerated movements of the chest wall suggesting pneumonia, and, when excited, breathing may be very rapid and the animal fall down in a coma and die. The lungs are generally waterlogged.

Complete recovery is generally slow, often taking a month or more, though the use of alpha-tocopherol acetate (one of the vitamin E fractions) has brought about marked signs of recovery in a few days. An initial dose of 600 milligrams, followed by 200 milligrams daily until recovery is complete, is recommended.

Grass silage, hay and distillers wet grains are useful natural sources of this vitamin.

Coughing Calves

Quite often calves become unthrifty and develop a dry, light cough which is exaggerated when they are disturbed by strangers or when they are being fed.

Whilst this condition is not infrequently associated with an outbreak of scours it may also occur independently and is thought in many cases to be due to a virus or a mycoplasma and accordingly must be distinguished from husk – which usually occurs at a later age.

Symptoms are not generally exaggerated though growth rate is delayed and recovery is slow. When a temperature is developed the use of antibiotics is to be recommended but, in general, feeding good fine hay, warm mashes and appetising foods containing stimulant powders brings about the most rapid recovery.

Remember that a good environment is far better than treatment.

"The Yellows"

A condition known as "the yellows" or leptospirosis is due to an infection by a small parasite. This resembles a spirochaete and leads a harmless existence in the rat and other wild rodents which, however, liberate it in large numbers in the urine. Food may well be infected by this method. When the parasite is ingested it penetrates into the body and passes to the liver and kidneys, causing damage to both of these organs.

Calves of from two to 10 weeks are more susceptible than older animals. Symptoms of dullness and loss of appetite appear from four to five days after infection, and the temperature may rise to 40·6°C. There is rapid loss of condition, accompanied by a varying degree of jaundice which shows itself as a yellow coloration around the eyes and mouth lining and is indicative of damaged liver. The urine may or may not be coloured with blood pigment, and scouring is not common.

When a positive diagnosis is made the injection of penicillin will have very satisfactory results, but do not forget to take steps to reduce, if not eliminate, the rat population. There is a marked summer/autumn incidence as in humans.

Disbudding

We ought not to leave this chapter without referring to two practices that go a long way to save trouble in later life. The first is disbudding, the second is a routine check on teats and udders to ensure that any abnormalities are corrected.

METHODS TO USE

Disbudding is rapidly becoming the thing. The hot iron method has to a certain extent given way to the modern electric cauteriser which, again, is very effective. An anaesthetic injection before the operation is, of course, necessary. In addition there is now available the dehorning collodion which can be painted on the horn buds but the risk of this spreading beyond the horn core is such as to bring this method into disrepute.

This should be applied before the calf is seven days old. Care should be taken that it does not touch the skin surrounding the horn base – a smear of vaseline is quite satisfactory for this – otherwise irritation may cause the calf to rub the spot and so weaken the action of the agent.

Disbudding is good advice. It means, in adult life, less disturbance, fewer injuries, less mastitis and more milk.

Before undertaking disbudding, however, it should be clearly understood that, under the Protection of Animals (Anaesthetics) Act, 1964, it is illegal to use the hot iron, electric iron or other mechanical means—such as cutting with a knife or gouge—without first ensuring that the calf has been effectively anaesthetized.

Supernumary Teats

Supernumary teats present no problem if dealt with in the young calf stage.

Get someone to hold the calf securely on its side, nip off the unwanted teat with a pair of curved surgical scissors and dress the wound liberally with tincture of iodine.

This is well worth doing. If left till the animal is a year or two old, an operation using anaesthetics will be necessary; if left till the animal calves, you may have the awkward problem of milking an extra quarter.

The normal teats are usually those which are properly placed. If there is any doubt as to which teats to take off, wait until there is appreciable udder development so that the relation of the teat with the tissue can be more clearly established.

CHAPTER V

DISEASES OF OLDER CALVES

I N recent years revolutionary changes have taken place in
the rearing of calves. They can either be reared on the
orthodox systems, either on the cow or bucket-fed on milk,
or the system of early weaning can be adopted. If carried out
properly, all these methods can be equally effective, and which
one is chosen depends upon the individual's preference and
available facilities on the particular farm. In all cases, however,
it is essential to permit the calf to have colostrum within six
hours of birth, and fresh water should be available from four
days of age. There is little advantage in giving calves water when
they are receiving large quantities of liquid, but where they are
being early weaned and put quickly on to solid foods, then
water should be readily available.

It goes without saying that the method adopted should be
carried out rigorously, but if calves are kept indoors their
quarters should be warm and comfortable.

Because it is now realised that calves are much tougher than
was originally believed, there is a trend toward rearing them
out of doors on grass from about a week old providing only a
primitive shelter of bales of straw.

Most proprietary foods fed will certainly be supplemented with the necessary vitamins A and D, but in other circumstances it would be an advantage if the synthetic vitamins were added to the meal or concentrates, and succulent foods offered, such as silage, kale and roots, to stimulate appetite. But, of course, these should not be given when the animals are on a controlled diet under the early-weaning system.

I consider that a calf should not have free access to drinking water until it is six or seven weeks old. If it has, the tendency is for it to indulge too freely and then be unwilling to take its full milk feeds. Thus it loses nourishment and may become pot-bellied.

IMPORTANCE OF MINERALS

Finally, ensure that minerals are provided, either in the form of licks or as a powder supplement included in the concentrate ration. In the case of a supplement only a "pinch" is really necessary per calf, or say, an eggcupful per ten animals per day.

An alternative to licks or powders is to use a fully mineralised proprietary milk substitute.

With good feeding along these lines and proper safeguards such as I have previously described against setbacks through disease in the early stages, you have the best opportunity of ensuring well-grown and healthy heifers with a far better chance of resisting troubles that are liable to affect them as they grow older.

Even so, these risks have to be faced. Let us see what can be done on the farm to prevent them as far as possible.

Again I come back to housing.

When your calves leave their rearing quarters, do you put them in bunches in an old barn or dirty, covered yard? If you do, it's asking for trouble.

Similarly, if you turn them out in spring to a small paddock that has been a permanent grass calf-pasture for many years, then again you are asking for trouble.

For all these places are invariably heavily contaminated with disease germs and parasites.

Do watch these points most carefully. It will more than repay you to go out of your way to provide light, airy and clean premises for your growing youngsters.

When you convert old buildings, scrape down any woodwork and scorch it thoroughly with a blowlamp. And, whether you use old premises or new, make it a rule to remove the dung and disinfect before a new batch of calves is introduced.

If you have a calf paddock such as I have described, then my advice is that you should provide a second one as quickly as possible and use it while you plough up and reseed the first. When you start to use it again, plough up the second and reseed that. Then rest each paddock for a year at a time, cutting the grass for hay or silage.

All these things matter in preventing disease.

WHEN TO TURN CALVES OUT

Where clean grass can be provided, many of the problems associated with turning calves out are automatically solved.

In such circumstances I would have no hesitation in turning out calves by day in clement weather when they reach the age of four weeks. Provided they receive a proper ration of milk and get some concentrates and hay, the exercise on pasture and a bite of fresh, clean grass will do them a world of good. Calves are more robust than some people think and thrive under quite rigorous outdoor conditions.

Should calves for any reason be prevented from being turned out until they are six months or more then they should be wormed with one of the modern remedies and vaccinated for husk.

Johne's Disease

It should also be your policy to keep growing stock away from adult cows.

Within the last few years we have learnt that Johne's disease – originally regarded as a disease of older animals – can infect calves. The germ may take 18 months to incubate and it is probable that a high proportion of the cases found in cows are, in fact, the result of infection in early life. After six months of age animals become increasingly resistant to infection.

There is, at present, no cure for the disease. Neither is it possible to detect all animals in the early stages of infection. Therefore, it's commonsense to try and prevent it infecting young stock.

That is why I am referring to it even at this early stage.

SYMPTOMS

Johne's disease is caused by a bacterium closely related to that of tuberculosis. It lives almost entirely in the bowel wall and associated glands. There it multiplies, causing irritation and subsequent thickening of the bowel wall.

This seriously upsets digestion. Food is not fully utilised, and the animal quickly loses flesh although eating well. Profuse scouring, sometimes with a bubbly appearance of the dung, is the other obvious symptom.

In advanced cases a soft swelling may appear between the bones of the lower jaw. This is described as "bottle jaw" and is not uncommon when animals are virtually starving, being unable to utilise their food.

The disease is widely distributed and causes considerable loss to farmers, often spreading quite rapidly through the herd. Affected animals shed the germs in large numbers, quickly contaminating pastures, water supplies and feedingstuffs.

PREVENTION

The best methods of preventing its spread are:

1. By fencing off all streams and ponds and supplying piped water to drinking troughs.
2. By setting drinking troughs as high as possible to avoid contamination.
3. By ensuring that food given indoors is not exposed to dung splashings.
4. By segregating young stock from adult stock.
5. Where the disease is a serious menace by removing the calf

from its dam at birth and feeding it the dam's colostrum from a bucket in a separate pen.

(Before removing the colostrum from the cow all dirt and dung which may contain the Johne's germs must be removed from the udder by thorough cleaning and disinfection.)

Alternatively, calves may be allowed to suckle under supervision. If this is done, then not only must the udder be properly cleaned; tie up the cow's tail and provide deep bedding to avoid dung splashing.

6. A valuable method of controlling this disease is to vaccinate the calf in the dewlap during the first few days of life and repeat this 18 months later. Protection appears to be provided only whilst the germs in the vaccine are active, which in practice means so long as the nodule is detectable. The size of the nodule is due to the nature of the oily base in which the vaccine is prepared and may at times be unsightly. However, further research has already suggested that this disadvantage may be overcome.

Approval to employ vaccination has to be secured from the Animal Health Branch of the Ministry of Agriculture through your vet as such a procedure seriously interferes with the interpretation of the tuberculin test, although in herds known to be free from tuberculosis the risk of masking a positive reaction is obviously unlikely.

It should be stressed that the employment of this method does not eliminate the necessity for taking the calf away at birth or controlling its feeding in the early days as the vaccination will not become effective at least for some weeks. It is an additional safeguard.

Further reference to Johne's disease in adult cattle occurs in chapter XIII.

Black Quarter

Another serious disease that occurs in calves between the ages of six months to two years is black quarter, or black leg. Often a single farm or a very localised strip of country has a bad reputation for this infection.

The disease frequently kills quickly without obvious symptoms, but sometimes there may be just a slight stiffness of movement prior to death. It is usually the best-doing calves that are affected.

The germ lives in the soil and is thought to get through the skin or to gain access to the body via the bowel and settle down in some muscular part of the animal. The shoulder or thigh is commonly affected; hence the name "quarter ill" is sometimes applied to it.

PREVENTION MEASURES

The part quickly becomes swollen and, on examination after death, this "abscess" or affected area is filled with gas and crackles when pressed with the hand. If it is opened, the flesh is rather darker than usual and a rancid smell can be detected.

There is no cure as generally there is no warning.

Vaccination is an effective preventive. If your farm is in an infected locality, you should arrange with your vet to inoculate each batch of young stock as a routine measure. Have the job done when calves are from three to four months old.

Calf Diphtheria

Yet another disease you may meet is calf diphtheria.

This is incorrectly named. The germ responsible is quite unlike the diphtheria bacillus. But the name has stuck, possibly because of the symptoms commonly shown.

Infected calves may slobber and throw back their cud. A thorn or piece of wire or displaced tooth may produce such an effect; but when this disease is the cause a close inspection will reveal extensive areas of decay round several teeth and extending even to the roof of the mouth. These decayed parts have a cheesy, greyish-yellow appearance.

Further symptoms may be nasal discharge, phlegm, etc, suggesting a lowered vitality and a possible vitamin A deficiency.

The only cure is a course of one of the sulphonamide drugs or

75

one of the antibiotics which can be administered by a veterinary surgeon. Both are effective.

Where the disease has been frequently encountered on the farm, then, as a general preventive, a proprietary vitamin and antibiotic supplement can be added to the calves' milk for the first few days after birth.

To reduce the incidence and in an effort to control infection it is desirable to clean buildings, spraying with a 5 per cent solution of washing soda. Finally swill out with a disinfectant and allow to dry out before fresh calves are introduced.

Conjunctivitis

Conjunctivitis or keratitis is simply an inflammation of the surface of the eye and may be due to contamination by dust-borne bacteria or may, in individual cases, be caused by a foreign body, such as a barley awn or oat flight or a piece of grit, becoming lodged in the tissues.

A more serious form of conjunctivitis may, however, be encountered, due to either phenothiazine poisoning or to a specific agent known as *Moraxella bovis*.

In conditions which are not yet clearly known calves being treated with phenothiazine can become sensitive to sunlight. This state of photosensitivity is associated with an interference with the normal breakdown of chlorophyl-like substances in the blood, trouble occurring in those places where capillary blood vessels are exposed to the ultra-violet rays of sunlight.

An affected calf cannot stand bright light and will discharge copious tears down the side of its face. In a very short time the tissues of the eye begin to break down and a small ulcerated surface develops, especially near the lower lid. Confine in dull light until better.

New Forest Disease

The other form of keratosis, which is encountered far more widely throughout the country and which has become known as New Forest disease because it was from this district that the first major outbreaks were reported, is somewhat similar to the foregoing but is associated with the specific rickettsial germ known as *Moraxella bovis*. This is readily transmitted by flies and directly from calf to calf when they are kept in close contact in batches, and by rubbing posts.

The broad spectrum antibiotics, penicillin, oxytetracycline and chloramphenicol are all effective in reducing the seriousness of this complaint, but success depends upon introducing treatment early. This consists of an injection into the sub-conjunctival tissues of the upper eyelid. Ointments may be used but recovery is very much slower. However, it is usually effective, even when the cornea is quite opaque, although it may take many weeks.

Moraxella bovis is known to survive in the conjunctival sac in untreated eyes for as long as $5\frac{1}{2}$ months. A drop of fresh cod-liver oil inserted from time to time encourages the growth of new tissue and the healing process. Spray round the eyes with a fly-repellent solution and keep the calves confined in a dark place.

An ulcer forms much more rapidly as a result of this infection than as in the case of phenothiazine poisoning and may quickly lead to protrusion of the lens of the eye.

As soon as the disease is suspected all calves on the premises should be treated. I would warn you that recovery is slow, but even where the eye appears white all over it will recover in time, although it may take six weeks.

Bovine Hyperkeratosis

This disease (also known as X disease) is most common in young stock, but cattle of all ages are susceptible. There is a copious discharge of tears, a nasal discharge, salivation, poor appetite and intermittent scouring. The animal assumes a state of marked depression and is apt to lose weight.

Perhaps the most striking symptom is the wrinkling of the skin, especially round the neck and withers, with a marked loss of hair.

Whilst there is evidence that this affliction is associated with a deficiency of vitamin A it may be induced by eating or by contact with a toxic chemical agent which may be present in

processed cereal concentrates, wood preservatives and petro-
leum machine lubricants.

The common ingredient of these substances is a highly-
chlorinated naphthalene. If rubbed on the skin this type of
compound may cause the symptoms described and the same
may happen when some of the material is eaten.

Parakeratosis

Although the existence of this skin condition has not been
confirmed in the British Isles, it is quite likely that cases do
appear from time to time and remain undiagnosed. This
resembles the disease in the pig, which is corrected by supplementing the ration with zinc.

The hair may be replaced by a dry, crusty surface over as
much as 40 per cent of the body including the muzzle, vulva,
anus, tail, ears, hind limbs, flanks, etc. In severe cases there is
a reddening of the lips, swelling of the hocks and knees and a
stiff gait.

Two grams of zinc sulphate given orally per week, for
several weeks, or one gram per week given by injection, bring
about recovery.

Parakeratosis should not be confused with heavy infestation
by lice.

Coccidiosis

Now let us deal with some of the parasites that are responsible
for trouble in growing stock.

Strictly speaking, a parasite is an individual that lives
harmoniously on or in its host. A few worms or coccidia in a
young animal do, in fact, pay for their keep. They encourage a
degree of immunity.

Unfortunately it is not always possible to limit the number.
More lodgers pile in, thinking to get hospitality, and symptoms
of disease appear. The animal ceases to put on weight, the coat
becomes staring and, though the appetite may remain good at

first, scouring develops, the eyes become sunken and death may ultimately occur.

An accurate diagnosis of the parasite responsible is, however, only possible after a microscopical examination of a sample of dung.

Coccidiosis is a disease generally associated with poultry. Actually, every animal and bird has its own specific coccidium. The common one of the calf – *Eimeria zurni* – can only affect calves. It will not attack poultry, rabbits or wild birds or anything else. But a calf may pick it up from another infected calf or cow, or from contaminated premises.

The symptoms of this disease are marked lassitude with blood in the droppings. These are not entirely characteristic signs (they may indicate Salmonella infection which I have already mentioned under calf scour and which will be dealt with more fully in a later chapter on causes of scouring) but, if they occur, you should be very suspicious.

Sulphamezathine has proved itself highly effective in the treatment of this disease. It is nevertheless important to establish proper diagnosis by having the dung examined.

Affected calves should be isolated. They should be treated with sulphamezathine by a veterinary surgeon and, after treatment, should be removed to clean quarters.

Bedding from their old quarters should be carried right away and buried deeply in a manure heap. The heat and ammonia engendered inside this will effectively destroy all the coccidia.

A final precaution to prevent a further outbreak is to wash down the pen walls with hot soda water, then rinse them and spray with dilute ammonia solution and allow to dry before bringing fresh stock into the pen.

Worms

Worms are more insidious than coccidia. They are most common in animals of from six months to bulling age.

The first symptoms are a rusty and staring coat and a slowdown of the rate of growth. There is not always scouring and where there is it may be intermittent. Then condition may be lost, a pot-bellied appearance becomes marked, and a swelling between the jaw bones develops known as "bottle jaw".

This last symptom is, in fact, characteristic of a state of starvation and may also be encountered in liver fluke infection and Johne's disease.

Here again, the trouble results from over-crowding, from contact with older stock or from grazing that "ever-so-handy" calf paddock that has been used for calves ever since anyone can remember.

A proportion of worm larvae will live in the soil for over a year. Many of them will even come to the surface after ploughing. And no amount of lime, chemicals or disinfectant will get rid of them.

The means of prevention are obvious: ploughing, reseeding and rotating the calf pastures.

The worms themselves will not be found in the dung and can only be seen by examining the walls or contents of the true stomach and small bowel after death. If a teaspoonful of mucus is scraped off these walls and allowed to smear round the inside of a glass jam jar by rotating it, the worms may be seen by holding the jar up to the light.

However, when infection is suspected it can be confirmed by examining a sample of dung under a microscope for the presence of worm eggs.

Larvae develop from these eggs and pass through several stages at a speed dependent upon the weather (moisture and temperature) and become infective to other animals. There is one stomach worm, however, which is much more important than any other. This is the *Ostertagia sps.* Treatment is so critical here that veterinary advice is necessary, but, in general, calves turned out in the spring need treating about the beginning of July and to be moved to clean pasture. Cattle on such pastures should be treated before being brought into their winter quarters or moved to clean ground. Information as to which parasites are present will help in planning treatment.

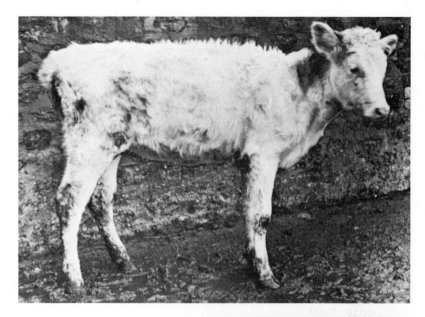

Above, typical
case of calf
affected with
worms.

Right: Calf with ringworm
at start of treatment; lower
picture shows same calf
28 days after treatment.
Below: Modern aerosol
spray said to be particularly
effective in treatment of
ringworm.

Photos (right) by kind permission
of I.C.I.

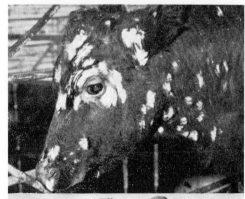

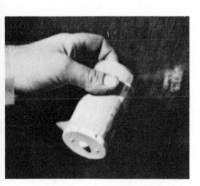

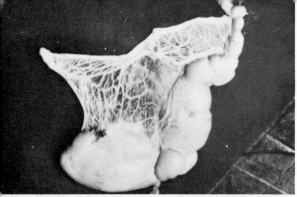

1. Stomachs of three-week-old calf. See from left to right rumen, reticulum, omasum and abomasum.

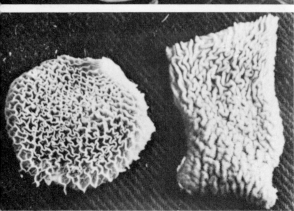

1(a). Digestive lining of rumen (right) and reticulum (left) of three-week-old calf.

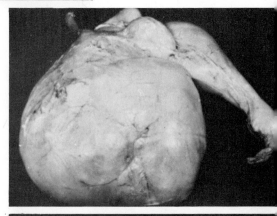

2. Stomach of calf at 10 weeks old—fed milk, nibble food and hay.

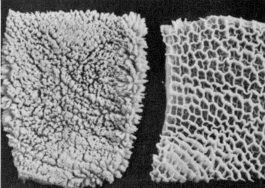

2(a). Digestive membranes of rumen (left) and reticulum (right) of 10-week-old calf.

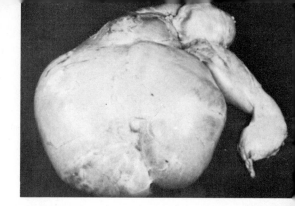

3. Stomach of 10-week-old calf—fed hay, early-weaning food and water only.

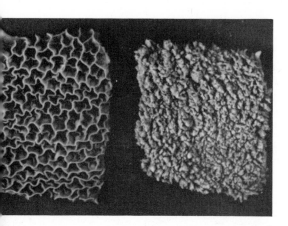

3(a). Digestive lining of rumen (right), and reticulum (left).

NOTE—

Marked growth of reticulum and abomasum and especially rumen at 10 weeks (photo 2), as compared with that at three weeks (photo 1).

Changes in the appearance of the digestive lining of the rumen and reticulum as between photos 1 and 2.

Greater development of all compartments and in particular the digestive linings as between photos 2 and 3.

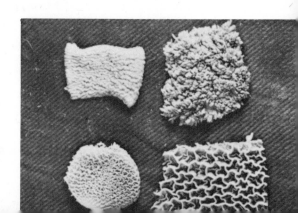

4. Comparison of digestive lining of rumen at three and 10 weeks of age (top of photo) and the reticulum at the same ages (bottom).

Photos: Vitameal0

Above, group of calves in New Zealand where turning out at very early age is practised, the calves preceding the cows in the paddocks to ensure freedom from parasitic troubles.

Below, photograph taken of experimental work at NIRD, Reading, with calves reared out-of-doors in early spring with only simple straw bale shelters for weather protection.

Husk or Hoose

This leads us to husk or hoose, a condition recognised to be widely distributed amongst cattle both young and old. Recent investigations indicate that fog fever in adult cattle (see chapter XIV) may well be a form of husk.

The clinical condition, however, is still primarily associated with young animals between six and eighteen months of age. They are most likely to contract infection during their first season at grass, though outbreaks are most commonly confined to the latter half of summer and the early months of autumn.

SYMPTOMS

Generally a number of animals are affected together, all showing symptoms of coughing of varying severity. Quite often these symptoms develop suddenly, some animals going into paroxysms of coughing which may result in sudden death – presumably due to the blocking of the air passages by masses of worms.

The majority, however, pass through an acute phase and then continue to cough for weeks or even months, during which time they lose condition and may become "bags of bones." Pneumonia often supervenes; bacterial infection establishes itself and causes death.

The method of treatment by injecting a mixture of fluids directly into the wind pipe in an effort to destroy or evict the parasites has fortunately given way to more effective and less distressing remedies.

MEANS OF CONTROL

Infection is almost always picked up from the pastures, though it is believed by some that the larvae of the worm can survive on hay and even in silage.

When infection occurs indoors, it is probable that contaminated dung has been left by other animals and that the larvae have subsequently hatched out, climbed up grass or corn shoots that grow in the corners of yards and buildings and have been eaten by the new inhabitants.

The adult worms of both sexes live and mate in the lungs. Their eggs hatch out and the larvae are coughed up, swallowed and passed out in the droppings, where they undergo a series of moults. Some, however, do stay in the body and get held up in the lungs and lymph glands.

The larvae (which are minute, being only about 0.5 mm long) prefer warm moist conditions and dislike strong light. For some time after reaching the ground they are motile and can move up grass stems wet with dew and rain.

In daylight and strong sunlight they move down towards the roots and ultimately tend to accumulate in the surface soil, where they pass through the changes referred to until they reach the infective stage. This may be anything from two to three weeks from the time they are shed in the droppings.

The larvae appear to be able to survive the winter and to resist climatic changes for six months or more.

Only turn young stock out onto fresh unused pastures. If, however, this is impossible, then turn them out for brief intermittent periods. No pasture dressing is worth while, but ploughing up and re-seeding will certainly help.

Very effective treatments for husk are now available. In the early stages of infection drugs such as diethylcarbamazine and methyridine will prove very effective, and the use of the oral vaccine is now general. The latter contains live larvae whose activity has been restricted by radiation so that, when freed in the alimentary tract, they are unable to migrate further than the associated lymph glands where they remain to stimulate the development of immunity. Whilst animals so treated do not show symptoms, they may nevertheless harbour parasites and be a source of infection to other animals on the same pasture.

Failure may result if:

1. Calves were already grazing infected pastures at time of vaccination.
2. Calves were freshly treated for worms thus killing the larvae of the vaccine.
3. Calves exposed to an excessively heavy natural infection.

4. Calves affected with other forms of pneumonia masking the picture.

Success of treatment depends on applying it early and at the right time. Once lung damage has become severe the way is open to infectious agents and other forms of pneumonia may appear.

Respiratory Infections

Respiratory conditions due to viruses and mycoplasmas are today a much more serious cause of loss than that due to husk worms. The activity of these agents has been aggravated by the increasing tendency to house large numbers of young stock together.

Transmission of infection is by water droplets following coughing and sneezing. In a pen where there are infected animals the air is continuously contaminated. Whether the problem becomes serious or not depends upon a number of factors, e.g. the number and age of animals in the pen. Young animals are more susceptible than older ones and the greater the number per square yard the greater will be the intensity of exposure. Ventilation plays a major part in keeping infection at a low level and comfortable temperatures around 10-16°C are desirable. Fluctuations should be avoided at all costs. A low roof helps to reduce draughts.

Some of the newer drugs appear to be helpful and vaccination is worthwhile, but emphasis is still upon proper housing and hygiene. Pens should be limited in size, 5-10 animals being an ideal unit and where possible there should be no means of direct contact between one pen and another. Suitably high walls will reduce the risks of infection which are far greater when animals can sneeze into each others' faces. An infected batch should be separated from a healthy batch by at least one pen space, but, of course, no affected animal should be brought into a house where healthy animals are present.

Sturdy or Gid

Another parasitic trouble is sturdy or gid. It is a common

trouble in sheep but, fortunately, is rare in cattle – only being occasionally encountered in older calves or heifers.

It is caused by the cyst of the dog tapeworm. The calf picks up the worm eggs when feeding; they develop inside the calf and the larval form migrates to the calf's brain.

The symptoms are a peculiar twisting and hanging of the head and a rolling gait. The affected animal loses appetite and slowly wastes. As there is no treatment, slaughtering is necessary.

However, the means of prevention are clear; farm dogs should be wormed regularly.

Ringworm

There is one more parasitic infection to discuss. It is ringworm.

This is a fungus disease, picked up from other infected animals or from sheds or yards that have not been properly cleaned out after being occupied by infected stock.

The ringworm spores get rubbed into the skin and begin to grow, throwing out lots of thread-like extensions. Yellowish-white, rounded, scurfy scabs soon develop.

Some regard this as an affliction of animals in a low state of health. This is not necessarily so. The cause may be the absence of some skin factor – a vitamin or mineral deficiency – but that has not yet been proved.

Limited control of the disease can be brought about by the use of any number of remedies. Whilst some favour the application of tincture of iodine to the sore after the scab has been removed, others have found the use of a 10 per cent solution of washing soda effective. When this is used care must be taken to keep the fluid out of the eyes.

After treatment with the soda an additional application of saturated solution of salicylic acid may be applied. Alternatively, a dressing of equal parts of creosote, linseed oil and carbolic acid may be used, precautions being taken to prevent this material getting onto the hands or skin of the operator or into the eyes.

Recent experience has shown that the inclusion of a griseo-fulvin premix in the ration is very effective against the ringworm fungus *T. verrucosum* and is more satisfactory than any of the remedies given above. Early introduction of treatment lasting for five days is necessary and recovered animals appear to have a high degree of resistance to reinfection.

Ringworm crusts should always be scraped off into a container and not onto the ground. The dressing may then be applied with a stiff brush and repeated a week later if necessary. (Remember that human beings are susceptible to ringworm, so wash hands and arms after the operation. If sores develop, cover them up with a wad of cotton-wool and soft bandage or adhesive plaster and ask your doctor for a prescription for Griseofulvin tablets. Take three 100-milligram tablets daily and you should be cured completely within two to three days. There may be side-effects in pregnant women so a doctor should always be consulted.)

When infected cattle have been successfully treated they should be moved out of the premises. Then rubbing posts and ledges should be scraped down and scrubbed with hot soda solution and later flamed with a blowlamp.

Bedding should be burned, walls washed down and woodwork creosoted.

Candidiasis

Another fungal disease of increasing importance is that due to the fungus *Candida albicans*, which is an internal complaint usually affecting young calves from two weeks upwards.

There may be very mild scour accompanied by slight dribbling of saliva from the mouth and evidence of discomfort during suckling. The muzzle and membranes of the mouth and tongue may show shallow, yellow ulcers with necrotic surfaces.

In more severe cases changes are present in the digestive tract, especially the stomach where large areas may be thickened and covered with caseous necrotic material. In such cases there may be severe and obstinate scouring. Localised centres of infection may also be present in the liver, lungs and kidneys, and the spores may be found widely dispersed in the body.

It is believed that prolonged high-level antibiotic treatment introduced for some other purpose may well precipitate candidiasis, for which there is no remedy. Although the fungal spores are widely distributed on hay and straw, the disease is fortunately quite rare.

FEEDING AFFECTS FERTILITY

Now I must emphasise a vitally important matter. It is the need for continued good feeding as the calf grows and particularly as she comes to the two critical stages of approaching conception and developing pregnancy.

The growing heifer should be fed for three things – to build up her skeleton, to increase her body size and to lay down a reserve.

Remember that she is going to be a mother. Demands on her will be great and she should be fed accordingly.

Do not regard appearance as a true guide. Even when keep is short, the outward "condition" of heifers may seem to be unaffected. But the first indication that something is lacking may come when you put the bull with them and you find they do not come in season or do not conceive.

Poor nutrition in the growing heifer can lay up a store of trouble. It may be responsible for sterility; it may cause difficult calvings; it may lead to retained afterbirths.

All this you want to avoid as far as possible. To do so you should ensure that your heifers are properly fed. They need an adequate maintenance ration of good hay or good silage. If you use hay for this, they need a daily feed of vitamin-rich succulent food such as silage or kale and, to provide "that extra something," they should have each day a pound or two (454 g or 907 g) of concentrates such as you feed for milk production.

As from May 1st, 1962, free vaccination against contagious abortion with Strain 19 was made available.

This vaccine should be given to the calf during the 120-day period after it has reached three months of age, that is, between the 90th and 180th day of life.

Strain 19 is proving itself even more effective than was originally thought, and it is hoped that by encouraging its extensive use at this stage, complete elimination of the disease will be greatly facilitated.

Cerebro-cortical Necrosis

Known for short as CCN this condition has been on the increase during recent years. Whilst young animals up to a year old are most commonly affected animals of almost any age above two months appear susceptible.

The symptoms are blindness, staggering and increased sensitivity. The animal may charge a wall or fence and collapse trembling. The temperature is normal, but there is loss of appetite and diarrhoea.

Post-mortem shows pale areas involving the rear part of the brain known as the cerebellum. This is the area which controls locomotion. Treatment by intra-muscular injections of the vitamin B complex, especially thiamine, has been remarkably successful in bringing about recovery even when the symptoms have been well advanced. This response suggests some interference with the production of or assimilation of the vitamin B complex within the alimentary tract.

Whilst lead poisoning can be ruled out the presence of a toxic agent which destroys or inhibits thiamine is suspected, the condition resembles that caused by horse-tail (equisetum) poisoning, though the explanation still remains unknown.

If the intake of this vitamin is marginal the presence of parasites such as worms or coccidia may aggravate the situation and bring early symptoms of a deficiency by using up the available vitamin and by interfering with absorption of that which is available in the food. Recent research has shown that certain conditions, as yet ill-defined, encourage the growth of rumen bacteria which destroy any thiamine present.

CHAPTER VI

STERILITY AND INFERTILITY

ALL good dairy farmers know the importance of having cows and heifers calve at the right time of the year. Regular breeding, like getting seeds in at the right time, is good farming. To a great extent the profit in dairy farming depends on it.

But it is not easy to achieve. Reproduction is a complicated process involving many factors, quite a number of which are still under intensive study and are, as yet, by no means clearly understood. Consequently it is not surprising that things do not always go according to plan on the farm.

When they don't, we have to look for the cause. It may lie with either partner – the bull or the cow, and in this chapter we will see what can be done to ensure that the cow is not at fault.

HOW REPRODUCTION WORKS

But let us first briefly set out the phenomena that lead up to and follow a heat period.

The whole process is intimately correlated by the pituitary gland at the base of the brain. One of the hormones that this gland produces is responsible for stimulating the development and shedding of eggs from the ovary at each heat period.

The eggs (which correspond to the white germinal spot on the yolk of a hen's egg) are always present in an immature form in the ovary, but as a result of hormone action, one usually develops at a time. As it develops it becomes swollen by fluid and looks rather like a blister. This is known as a Graafian follicle.

Shortly after the animal has gone off heat, the Graafian follicle bursts and liberates the egg which then falls into the opening of the fallopian tube. It then passes down the tube towards the tip of the horn or the uterus.

At this stage, if all goes well, the egg is fertilised, the nuclear material of one sperm from the bull becoming completely united with it, after which it steadily develops in the womb.

WHAT CORPUS LUTEUM DOES

Immediately after the follicle ruptures to release the egg, some tissue starts to grow in the crater that is left in the ovary. By about the eighth day this is about the size of a cherry and constitutes what is known as the *corpus luteum* or "yellow body."

One function of the tissue is to prevent any further shedding of eggs from the ovary for the entire period that the cow carries

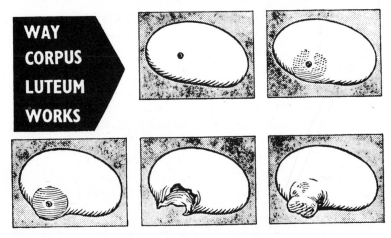

WAY CORPUS LUTEUM WORKS

Diagram sequence shows egg migrating towards wall of ovary, fluid beginning to accumulate round egg, egg surrounded by fluid, rupture of follicle to release egg, development of corpus luteum in cavity.

her calf. If conception does not take place when the egg is shed, the *corpus luteum* steadily degenerates into a very small body secreting so little hormone that it is unable to postpone the onset of the next heat period.

WHEN THINGS GO WRONG

Occasionally this well-ordered routine goes wrong. The Graafian follicle may not rupture and release the egg just when it should and it may remain in the ovary and form a cyst. Or the *corpus luteum*, which should disappear after a failure to conceive or after the birth of a calf, may fail to disappear.

In either event the ovary cannot release further eggs. Therefore the animal cannot be got in calf. In the former case heat periods become frequent but matings are sterile. Some 20 per cent of animals may show exaggerated female behaviour and a few the masculine digging or pawing syndrome. In the latter case the animal fails to come into season.

Such conditions can only be determined by expert examination. Their correction, too, depends on expert manipulation to rupture a cyst or to squeeze out the *corpus luteum*. The utmost care is essential in such an operation or serious damage may be done, so it should be left to a veterinary surgeon.

Both these conditions normally respond to treatment, but there is a cystic condition of the ovaries that is difficult to remedy. It is the one that causes nymphomania – a state of being continually in season and of taking the bull at any time but without conceiving.

This, if treated in the early stages, may be put right, but usually if the trouble is too well established the only thing to do with such an animal is to have her slaughtered.

In this respect, as in others, a careful review of the feeding regime is very important. Increasing experience with the metabolic profile test (see elsewhere) suggests that anoestrous and/or cystic ovary trouble may be of nutritional origin. In particular, the energy value of the ration needs to be carefully checked.

Another cause of infertility is associated with the hormone that controls the heat period. It may happen, particularly in heifers, that this hormone is lacking and no heat period takes place. In such cases the matter is usually corrected by an injection of the hormone. But, after such an injection, do wait for the animal to get into the proper rhythm of heat periods before you have her served.

To serve her at the first heat period that follows is unwise. This is an "induced" heat rather than a true heat and the animal may not conceive as a result of being served at this time.

Further, if she is served and does not come into season again, you may be lulled into thinking that she is in calf, whereas further treatment may, in fact, be required.

SIGNS OF HEAT PERIOD

Where there are no abnormalities such as those described a cow will come regularly into season (showing signs of heat) every 19 to 21 days. The animal shows slightly increased excitability, is apt to mount other cows or let herself be mounted, and strings of clear mucus frequently pass from the vagina. The temperature is slightly increased and milk yield is slightly reduced.

The phenomena of coming into season may be delayed in animals that are poorly fed or affected with parasites, Johne's disease or similar debilitating conditions. Poor feeding and the lack of light associated with the short winter days may also retard the appearance of heat or cause it to be so slight (what is called a lightning heat) that one fails to notice it.

The heat or oestrous periods are not the same for every cow. Fifteen per cent of animals show cycles less than 17 days; of these, those that are between 8-10 days in length are more likely to conceive than the others.

INFERTILITY FROM INFECTIONS

Infertility can, of course, arise from infections.

Three of these – contagious abortion, trichomoniasis and vibriosis – will be dealt with in detail in later chapters, but here

I will give you my general advice about them to help you to minimise the risk of infertility due to them.

In the case of an abortion, especially one that occurs at or after the third month, it is always wise to have a blood test carried out for contagious abortion and to send the foetus to a laboratory for examination. Even if the test is negative a further test three weeks later is desirable.

A check-up at this time may save you a lot of money and inconvenience by giving you an early diagnosis. Should either test reveal an infection, get veterinary advice regarding treatment and subsequent procedure relating to services, isolation, control measures, etc.

I particularly emphasise the need for quick action because of the risk of chronic endometritis developing – a serious cause of infertility. This is an inflammation of the lining of the womb which may result from an infection following an abortion.

Trichomoniasis

Trichomoniasis is to be suspected if several animals start coming into season 9 to 16 weeks after what you have considered to be effective services.

If this happens, you should ask your veterinary surgeon to examine the discharge just before the heat period is due. Infected animals may recover naturally if they are not served for some months, but the trouble can be more quickly corrected by womb irrigation.

The bull must also be examined. The treatment of young animals up to five years old is usually successful though subsequently results get poorer, but the disease has now very markedly declined since the vastly extended use of A.I. Bulls are very carefully tested before semen is issued.

Vibriosis

This is a true venereal disease which – as will be seen in a later reference – has many features in common with contagious abortion. But its cause – and its treatment – is quite distinct. That is why, before proceeding with any scheme for the control of infertility, an accurate diagnosis of the trouble is essential –

for which purpose it is necessary to send specimens of fresh afterbirth and vaginal mucus samples to a laboratory.

Leucorrhoea or Whites

Another infection that causes infertility is leucorrhoea or "whites." The name helps you to diagnose it. There is a thick discharge from the womb. It is usually dead white but may have a yellowish tinge.

Its presence means that there is an inflammation of the womb.

It may appear after a bad calving or follow when an animal has retained her cleansing. It is sometimes attributed to the bacterium responsible for summer mastitis – *C. pyogenes*. But many scientists are of the opinion that in such cases this germ is not primarily the cause; they believe there may be a predisposing factor, possibly nutritional, that lowers the animal's resistance and allows the infection to get the upper hand.

And, where there is inflammation of the womb, neither ovum nor sperms will survive. Consequently the animal fails to breed.

Some degree of success in the treatment of this disease has been achieved by irrigating the womb with a variety of solutions, including Lugol's iodine, lactic acid, streptomycin, etc. As there is some evidence to suggest that iodine may be lacking in these circumstances the addition of 30 grains of potassium iodide a day to the steaming-up ration of the in-calf animal is suggested for a week prior to calving.

Metritis

This is an inflammation of the womb and generally results from an infection establishing itself after some injury or physiological upset. Leucorrhoea or whites is, in fact, an indication of the existence of metritis – a condition that occurs in trichomoniasis and contagious abortion and may need special treatment by way of irrigation as already indicated in connection with leucorrhoea.

It is also important to look into the nutritional status of the animal as well as to see whether enough minerals and vitamins are being given – an aspect of infertility which is dealt with at greater length later in this chapter.

Pyometra

This is an accumulation of pus in the womb resulting from an infection. The cervix or exit from the womb has closed and prevented the material from being liberated.

Pyometra is commonly associated with trichomonas infection or may be due to streptococci, staphylococci, pyogenic bacteria, all of which become established when the womb lining has been damaged.

The use of hormones to relax the cervix is common in this condition; when this has taken place irrigation can then be carried out.

Even for the expert it is not easy to decide whether a womb is full of pus or whether the animal is in calf. Whilst a pyometra exists there will be no signs of heat, which may lead you to suspect that everything is satisfactory. This is one of the many reasons why I recommend you to have a routine pregnancy diagnosis made on your herd every three or four months.

Cervicitis

The cervix is the enlarged opening of the womb, extending into the vaginal cavity. An inflammation of this organ is generally secondary to a metritis or vaginitis. The cervix becomes enlarged and red in colour and in this state will prevent the passage of any sperm at time of service. The trouble may result from laceration of the neck of the womb during calving.

Where the condition becomes chronic and difficult to cure, AI may be successful in bringing about a normal pregnancy as, with AI, the sperms can be deposited beyond the obstruction.

Cystic Ovaries

Chronic inflammation of the ovaries may lead to the development of cysts in them or in their becoming fibrous. The affected animal will either show no signs of heat or be a nymphomaniac.

Cystic ovaries are believed to be associated with hormone upsets or nutritional deficiencies and in the former respect it is of interest to note that cystic ovaries and ovarian dysfunction may occur in cows fed on lucerne, probably due to the presence of hormone-like substances. Fishmeal and meat-and-bone meal seem to be particularly useful in this respect; they are believed to be beneficial in adjusting the hormone balance through improving liver function, possibly due to their high methionine content.

I shall be making fuller reference later on in this chapter to the importance of the right sort of proteins in combating infertility.

Salpingitis

This is a name given to an inflammation of the fallopian tubes. As these are so very small any inflammation has such a slight effect that it is difficult to detect the change by manipulation and no outward indication is given except that the cow, though coming into heat regularly, does not hold.

The cause is an infection which has spread up from the womb – possibly as a result of metritis – and has caused a thickening of the fallopian tubes so that no ova can pass down when shed from the ovary and no sperm can pass up. Rest is the best treatment though irrigation with Lugols iodine and antibiotic injections should be tried.

Vaginitis

There is a good deal of doubt as to whether vaginitis is a primary condition or is secondary to metritis or cervicitis. The inflammation is found on the wall of the vagina which is congested and very often spotted with small ulcers. If the lips of the vagina are parted these changes can be seen on the lining of the mucus membrane.

In the more acute cases a cow will be restless with her tail lifted and will occasionally eject small quantities of mucoid pus. Most cases however are mild and show no symptoms.

This is true of the type known as granular vaginitis where a ring of small raised glands can generally be felt just inside the opening. This condition is temporary and usually physiological in origin, but a virus has been implicated in some cases (see

95

under infectious bovine rhinotracheitis). So often there is no discharge accompanying these changes.

WOMB IRRIGATION

In all instances where there are discharges you can introduce into the vagina one of the standard antiseptic pessaries as a precautionary measure, but this alone will rarely be enough.

Most chronic discharges have a deeper origin and may need womb irrigation which should only be undertaken by a veterinary surgeon. A catheter has to be used and there is considerable risk of causing damage by puncturing the vaginal wall or womb with the point of the instrument and setting up a peritonitis that may be fatal.

Another method of treatment is to allow six months' sexual rest followed by the use of AI. This, however, will be useless if there is still any discharge, so you should wait at least until one normal heat period has occurred after discharges have been cleared up.

I do wish to stress the importance of immediate attention when a discharge from the genital organs is observed or if you suspect that there is some inflammation. If this is neglected it may lead to pyometra, to cystic or fibrous ovaries, etc, etc – and these, as I have already indicated, are far more difficult matters to put right.

OTHER CAUSES OF INFERTILITY

Unfortunately this does not end the list of causes of infertility. We now have to consider those that arise through environment and especially through feeding.

Here it is well to remember the great demands we make on our cows today. We don't let them calve in the season they would choose if left to themselves and we want, over and above the 60 or 70 gallons (273 to 318 l) that would normally be secreted for the calf, from 600 gallons (2,728 l) to as much as 2,000 (9,090 l) and more for sale.

Cows have responded amazingly to the improved scientific management of today and their capacity to give more and more milk seems almost limitless.

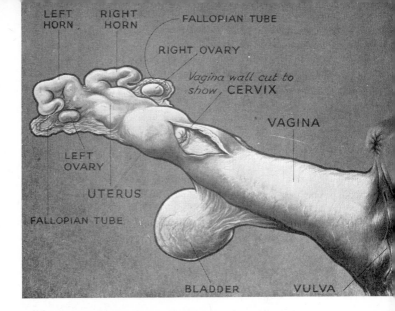

COW'S REPRODUCTIVE SYSTEM

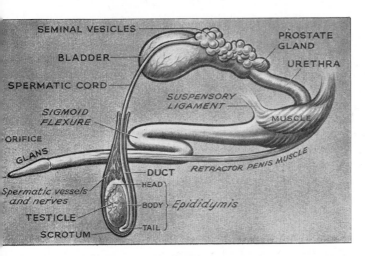

BULL'S REPRODUCTIVE SYSTEM

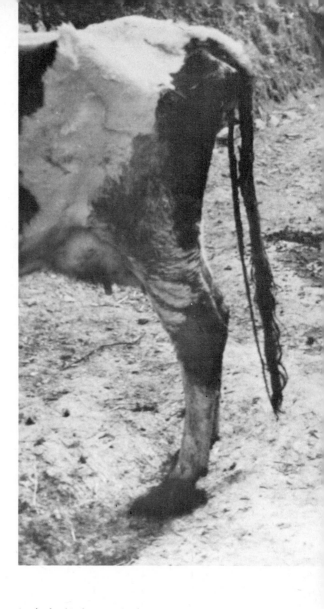

This sort of thing—a retained afterbirth—may lead to many problems later. Expert attention may be necessary; best farm treatment is exercise, good feeding and the use of pessaries.

DEALING WITH MILK FEVER

This series of pictures shows an affected cow receiving appropriate veterinary treatment.

Top picture illustrates typical condition of affected cow; subsequent photographs show respectively—raising the cow to allow for propping with straw bales; application of milk fever injection into the skin over shoulder and ribs; direct injection into the veins; a complete rotation of the cow is advisable every two or three hours to prevent her from becoming blown.

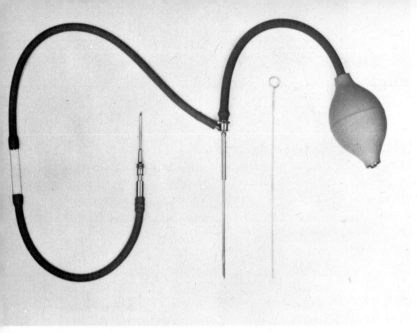

Milk fever outfits—as shown above—can be purchased from veterinary chemists. Right-hand picture shows the flutter valve used with the apparatus.

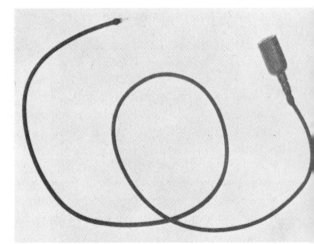

Photos: Boots Pure Drug Co., Ltd.

Nevertheless we have got to realise that there are external forces that play an important part in the mating and breeding habits of birds and animals and we have to be careful in our commercial exploitation – of cows in particular – not to change the balance of these forces, especially of environment and feeding, too rapidly.

The above remarks may apply and explain why conception rates are so frequently bad in newly constituted herds. Cows purchased from many sources and accustomed to many different environments are regrouped under a fresh management regime.

INFLUENCE OF LIGHT

The influence of light is now regarded as significant. It appears to affect, through the eyes, the pituitary gland which in turn controls the sex cycle. Hens lay better as the days grow longer, and ewes can be persuaded to take the ram out of season if illumination is drastically altered by artificial means. Even the germination of seeds is influenced by light and darkness.

So it is understandable that heifers are difficult to get in calf during the winter months and cows sometimes have short and possibly "silent" heats that pass unnoticed, when the ovary produces the egg but the cow does not show any outward sign of being in season.

We have not yet reached the stage of advocating artificial light treatment for cows and heifers on a wide scale, but tests are being made which may improve winter fertility.

This question of light is one that the dairy farmer must bear in mind. It is in this respect that out-wintering and yarding in open yards have advantages over keeping cows and bulling heifers indoors during this period of the year.

Similarly it is an advantage from this point of view to let the bull run with the cows or heifers although it may complicate the problem of bringing calving times within precise limits.

But, where a farmer is repeatedly meeting the difficulty of "catching" the cows at the right time, it may pay to let the bull do the job. A calf a bit too early is better than no calf at all, and it is always possible to delay turning out a particular animal or to keep her segregated from the herd if you are not willing for her to be served.

INFLUENCE OF FEEDING

The influence of feeding on fertility is much more complicated.

This is a subject that is today receiving considerable scientific attention, particularly from the point of view of determining the influence of individual components of the food.

All dairy farmers know how effective the first bite of grass is and how a cow or herd breeding problem often disappears when grazing starts in the spring. It is thought that oestrogens in young grass may stimulate oestrus, just as they stimulate milk production.

Some research workers stress the stimulating effect of the proteins on the pituitary gland that controls the shedding of eggs from the ovary, but it may be that it is the quality – the biological value – of these proteins that is important.

RATIONS MUST BE "BALANCED"

We know there are some proteins that are suitable for milk production and some that are suitable for beef production. Perhaps there is one that is right for breeding.

Similarly, there is a lot of circumstantial and laboratory evidence about the part that minerals and vitamins play, or appear to play, in the control of infertility, a state of affairs that is becoming slowly more clear cut.

However, the first and foremost rule on the farm must be to ensure that the maintenance and production rations are properly balanced in the broad sense of protein, carbohydrates and fats. Under-nourishment arising from a shortage of one or more of these will cause a state of sub-normal health that may lead to infertility.

But beyond this there are the problems of finer balances in feeding, particularly with regard to minerals and vitamins. Practical advice in these matters is not quite so straightforward.

There is increasing evidence to suggest, however, that the requirements of the dairy cow in production may outstrip the available nutrient intake, resulting in disturbed fertility – in other words, when the level of milk production is in excess of that provided for by the production ration. It may be that the cow is incapable of ingesting sufficient quantity of food to satisfy production needs – a circumstance which is more likely to arise under conditions of intensive grazing systems. The starch equivalent of good summer grazing is just as inadequate for high-yielding cows as is its mineral content. As a result there may be an increase in the number of services per conception, abnormally long intervals between services, and even abortions.

The steaming-up period provides an ideal opportunity for building up reserves and should be taken, but the requirement of the cow alters when she suddenly comes into milk. More energy is necessary in the latter circumstances and an inclusion of ground maize at this stage is highly beneficial; there is, in fact, a case for two distinct rations to meet the demands of the different metabolic states.

Attention has recently been drawn to the weight of animals during the lactation period. There seems to be a significant relationship between increasing weight and improved conception to first service during this period. But this fact emphasises still further the importance of feeding the right ration during this critical period. (See also Metabolic Profile – Production Disease).

Furthermore, after service and until the embryo has become properly established on the floor of the womb (which occurs about the 17th day), the cow needs special care. A dramatic change in ration or environment or any other marked stress at this time may well have an adverse effect, with the animal returning to service.

We know, for example, that calcium and phosphorus should be in certain proportions in the total ration. If the ratio is too wide either way trouble may arise.

And there should be adequate quantities of not only calcium and phosphorus and manganese but also of the trace elements copper and iodine, bearing in mind that if there is an excess of calcium then the availability of all these is likely to be suppressed.

The result may be an induced deficiency and a consequent disturbance of the breeding mechanism.

So you see trouble may occur as a result of an excess of or a deficiency of one or more of these elements; thus it is clearly important to ensure that they are all present in adequate amounts in a well-balanced ration.

EFFECT OF EXCESS CALCIUM

Dairy farming developments in recent years have tended to disturb this balance. There has been a great increase in the application of lime; and certain fodder crops, rich in calcium – notably kale, clover and lucerne – have achieved considerable popularity. The amounts of them now fed are much higher than formerly.

It may well be that the sum total of these practices has disturbed the balance of feeding and has aggravated the problem of infertility in some herds.

We know for instance that in certain years a factor appears in kale which has the effect of suppressing the availability of iodine. We know that this may result in calves being born dead although fully formed and at full time. The oestrogenic effect of kale has also been demonstrated associated with uterine enlargement.

Other members of the brassica family, such as rape and cabbage are also thought to contain similar goitrogens from time to time. Presumably these substances upset the work of the thyroid gland, thus inducing a temporary deficiency resulting in a mild goitre.

OTHER MINERAL PROBLEMS

It has been known for some time that, in experimental laboratory mice, a lack of manganese results in delayed ovulation. Now there has been growing evidence of manganese deficiency in crops – grey speck or stripe in oats, speckled yellows in sugar beet and yellow spot in peas – and so it is possible that there may in some instances be a basic deficiency of manganese in the cow's ration.

This mineral may also be locked up when there is an excess of calcium in the soil or made unavailable in the cow's ration.

All this does not mean that we should abandon progressive practices. Indeed, it must be pointed out that while liming may render a soil too alkaline and cause valuable trace elements such as copper, cobalt and manganese to become so "locked up" that they are not available to animals through the crops, the same effect may occur in soils that are too acid and are in need of lime.

What we have to do is to ensure that, as far as possible, farming does not disturb the balance of essential factors.

To boil this down to practical advice, I would say this: first make use of ADAS for soil tests as often as required and follow their guidance as to what fertilisers your soil requires; secondly, in feeding your cows try and ensure a reasonable variety of foods – to feed an excess of any one food may lead to upsetting the balance of vital minerals and vitamins and so create a problem of infertility.

Soil surveys have shown that the levels of trace elements are generally of such a low order that crops grown on them take up insufficient for the modern dairy cow in full production. It is therefore essential to ensure that the compound ration is adequately fortified. This applies particularly to manganese and phosphorus, but only to iodine in special cases.

Copper deficiency, once rare, has suddentlly become common due to the increased popularity of beef production, resulting in many herds being run solely on grass.

It is frequently beneficial to introduce from 7 to 10 per cent of a good quality meat-and-bone meal or fishmeal into the winter ration where there is a tendency for anoestrous (lack of signs of heat) to be widespread in the herd.

Individual cows can be tried with a teacupful of fishmeal a day on their concentrates or 28 lb (12·7 kg) calcium diphosphate may be included per tonne of food. Some benefit should accrue in six weeks.

A good general additional safeguard is to feed one of the better compounds already containing adequate minerals or one of the well-recognised complete mineral supplements.

The latter can easily be given during the winter in farm-mixed concentrate rations; in spring and summer when the cows are milking largely off grass the problem has been overcome by some farmers by feeding at milking time the mineral mixture in a "carrier" of moist sugarbeet pulp or cheap fodder ground up finely, mixed with the minerals, and damped down.

As well as adequate protein levels it is now clear that energy levels are equally important in maintaining a proper sexual rhythm. If insufficient, it may result in frequent "turnings" or simple anoestrus.

But on some farms special mineral problems do arise which can only be dealt with by the use of specially-prepared mineral supplements fortified in the appropriate manner – for instance by additional copper in copper-deficient areas.

If such a problem does arise, one that seems to defy diagnosis, then take advantage of the special services available. Your own vet can obtain any help he may need from a number of different sources in his efforts to correct matters.

IMPORTANCE OF VITAMINS

In connection with this problem we must not forget the important part which vitamins may play.

Vitamin E, for instance, has been associated with breeding for many years and has been known to be essential for the maintenance of a healthy womb lining. Its influence in the body is however now known to be much more general, the effect upon the womb being only indirect. Vitamin A must not be overlooked in this respect, too.

It is also probable that vitamin D plays a much greater part through its association with the absorption of the minerals, calcium and phosphorus from the bowel. An injection of vitamin D_3 (5-10 million units) appears to encourage the onset of heat in cows which have not been in season for some months, and to improve the conception rate.

In the British Isles the natural synthesis of vitamin D through the exposure of the skin to sunlight is limited to less than half of the year – the sun's rays being too weak and passing through such a thick atmosphere during the rest of the year that the ultra-violet rays are filtered out.

This is a good reason to ensure that the daily ration contains adequate supplies of this vitamin. Hay is generally a good natural source. In this respect, the longer it has been sun-bleached the better!

Again the question of vitamins in relation to infertility is one which may call for special veterinary diagnosis in co-operation with the advisory service now available.

Anatomical Abnormalities

There is one more aspect of breeding problems that should be mentioned. It concerns anatomical abnormalities.

Some can be overcome by using AI, as in the case of a slack vagina which obstructs the passage of the penis of the bull.

Recto-vaginal fistula, or a damaged passage open to the air, (fortunately rare) where the opening of the vagina remains permanently apart, is usually due to mechanical damage at calving. The cervix may also be relaxed, allowing air to pass to and fro.

It is seldom possible to get affected animals in calf and they should be disposed of.

Freemartins

Other abnormalities – such as the incomplete development of the sexual organs as found in freemartins (heifers born as twins with bulls) – cannot be corrected or overcome.

It is usually considered a waste of time to attempt to breed from the female freemartin. The genital passages are rudimentary, a fact which can be confirmed within the first week of life. The vulva will appear as though sewn up in such a fashion that it is only possible to insert a thin pencil at the lowest point. When this is pushed in it meets a complete obstruction within an inch or two.

Post-mortems on such animals show that there is only a rudimentary womb.

This abnormality is considered to be due to the suppressing influence of the male hormones circulating in the communal blood supply of the two calves whilst still within the womb. The male sex organs develop before those of the female and prevent the latter from achieving normal development.

It is useful to be able to detect a female freemartin in early life to avoid the great disappointment and loss of money when later it is discovered to be incapable of breeding.

"White Heifer" Disease

There is an abnormality found most commonly in white animals of the Shorthorn breed and called "white heifer" disease. This may vary from undeveloped vagina and genital tract to a persistent hymen across the mouth of the womb.

In all such cases the animal may not be able to take the bull and will certainly not breed. Fattening for slaughter is the best plan where possible, but where a persistent hymen is the only abnormality a surgical operation can be carried out to relieve the condition.

VALUE OF A BREEDING RECORD

Now this is a long list of infertility troubles. But it will help you, I think, to appreciate that infertility is not a simple problem to be solved by a magic powder or a bottle of medicine.

It may arise from any single one of a hundred and one causes, many of which you can control by good management on the farm, but most of which, when they do arise, can only be put right by accurate diagnosis and treatment by professional hands.

But do not ignore the value of a well-kept breeding record. It will be a great help to you in better herd management and, should you have to seek help with breeding troubles, it will reduce your vet's work considerably and help to guide him to the cause. It should not only state service and calving dates but should give full information about the presence of discharges, abortions, retained afterbirth and the treatment given in each case.

To avoid gaps and increase efficiency, records are invaluable and in this respect the use of an automatic heat detector such as the "Siresine" with a teaser (vasectomized) bull is worth considering for a large herd. A spring-loaded ball is used, fixed in a small holder and attached to the lower jaw of the teaser. When pressed on the haunches of an animal in season it leaves a coloured streak. When such marks also occur on the withers and other parts of the body it is all the more likely that the animal is in season.

Another and increasingly popular method of spotting heat is the use of the "Kamar" detector*. This has a special role to

PREGNANCY TEST

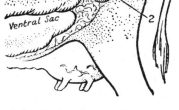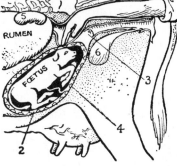

These sketches illustrate the veterinary surgeon's method of determining pregnancy. Left: In the early stages the one horn will feel larger than the other. At three months it might be 3-3½ in. (76-89 mm) across compared with a normal ½ in. (13 mm). Right: Palpating the growing calf. The test is, of course, made through the rectum.

1—rectum; 2—uterus; 3—cervix; 4—cotyledon; 5—kidney, 6—bladder.

* The detector consists of an oval of canvas, 11 x 5 cm, to which is attached a plastic dome, 8 x 1.5 cm in size. Inside the dome is a plastic tube containing a red dye. Sustained pressure exudes the dye from the tube, and the dome becomes wholly red. The detector is sealed to the spinal ridge some few inches towards the head from the root of the tail.

play in animals not seen on heat up to 45 days after calving or after being discovered empty following pregnancy diagnosis.

Such artificial methods may, however, be dispensed with if three half-hour periods are set aside each day to observe animals! To facilitate observation animals should not be feeding and not in the collecting yard or pen. The times selected are 8-8.30 am, 2-2.30 pm and 9-9.30 pm. Though one's first reaction may be that this is tedious, there is usually staff on duty, at least during the day, and experience has proved the system to pick up 90 per cent of animals in heat as against the present 70 per cent success scored by casual and irregular observation. No observations need be made in the months of August, September and October if the herd is geared to winter milk production. This system is of considerable economic benefit and greatly improves profit.

However, the introduction of the controlled breeding system by the use of prostaglandin can greatly simplify matters. Oestrus will occur 2-3 days after an injection except in those animals in which oestrus has occurred within 5 days. A further injection eleven days later to all the animals in the group will, however, ensure that all are ready for AI or service in 72 hours. Thus anxiety about heat detection is removed and concentration of the calving 'season' facilitates management.

This system is ideal for beef suckler-cow units. The treatment should only be applied to normal animals and is no remedy for infertility. Suckler cows tend to be slow in coming into oestrus after calving and should not be injected before such signs appear. Heifers should not be treated until sexually mature and properly cycling and, further, they should not be less than 60 per cent of their adult body weight.

PREGNANCY DIAGNOSIS

Finally, if you want an insurance policy, I suggest again the very sensible one of having pregnancy diagnoses carried out at regular intervals – say every three months – or at least as often as circumstances suggest.

It is a job for the vet as it requires considerable experience and a detailed anatomical knowledge. Ninety days after service is the ideal time for this examination. After six months the foetus is too far forward to feel, but at this stage it should be possible to feel the pulse of the arteries inside the abdomen. Experienced clinicians can detect pregnancy, especially in heifers, at the 7th or 8th week of gestation.

Biological tests are proving increasingly efficient. The pregnancy hormone progesterone level rises in the blood and milk immediately after oestrus. If pregnancy is established it remains high; if not, it declines again. So, if there are no signs of heat 21 days after AI or service, a milk sample taken on the 28th day should give a positive result. Results are as yet not as clear-cut as might be expected, (negatives are more reliable than positives) but this approach to pregnancy diagnosis is worth discussing with your veterinary surgeon. To know the state of affairs early will save time and money.

CHAPTER VII

ART OF BULL MANAGEMENT

THE maintenance of fertility in the bull is mainly a farm job. It depends, even more than with cows, on the way you feed and the methods of management you employ. And you've got to start at the beginning – right from the day the bull is born.

A generous diet for the young bull calf and proper treatment as he develops are the foundations of a long, active and useful life.

You may wish to rear the calf on a nurse cow, or to bring it up on the bucket, but you could use the early-weaning system if you wished, as this is perfectly satisfactory. It is necessary to do everything that is possible within reason to give the calf a good start in life, and that includes regular exercise each day if the calf is reared indoors. This helps to tame the bull and prevent him from being temperamental later.

HOUSING THE YOUNG BULL

As far as the calf is concerned, if you have to house it instead of giving it free run with a nurse cow then the advice that I gave on housing heifer calves applies.

Useful
Bull Pens

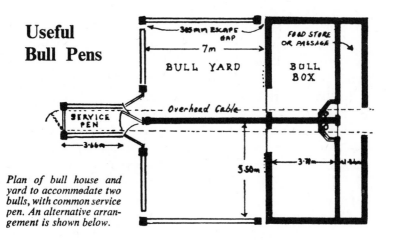

Plan of bull house and yard to accommodate two bulls, with common service pen. An alternative arrangement is shown below.

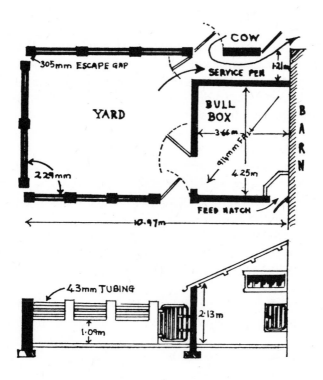

109

The premises should be light and adequately ventilated. They could, with advantage, be a little more roomy than is customary for heifers; and it would certainly pay to provide a sound, level floor because of the importance of well-developed legs and feet in the bull. Uneven floors such as those found in old cobbled stable premises are to be avoided at all costs.

As the calf nears the age of service, he should be introduced to the premises he is to occupy as an adult.

Here I am going to be very severe on those farmers (fortunately there are now not many) who still think that some old dungeon is good enough for the bull or that it will do to keep him permanently tied up in an old bullock stall or at one end – usually the darkest end – of a dark cowhouse.

These practices cannot be condemned too strongly.

In the first place we know that light is an important factor in health and well-being. It has something to do with vigour and virility and plays a vital part in stimulating body processes.

Secondly, there is the adverse factor of being confined or even tied up so that movement is restricted or almost prohibited. That, too, weighs against normal health and is the main reason why a bull gets temperamental and displays some independence when he is taken out to serve a cow or heifer.

LET HIM SEE WHAT'S HAPPENING

So, make it a rule on your farm that the bull gets a chance to stretch his legs and see the world. Give him a proper bull pen with an exercising yard. If there isn't enough room in the yard, then take him for a walk every day.

Undue confinement with inability to see and take part in the activities of the rest of the herd may lead to depression, and exhaustion following masturbation, often precipitated by the herd passing to and fro.

You will be more than repaid by the gain in health and fertility that results by paying attention to these matters.

MALE GENITAL SYSTEM

Having got the bull properly housed at about 10 months

of age, the question of using him for service then arises. Here it will help if we first of all study how the male genital system works. The illustration facing page 96 will help to make the process clear.

The testicles each contain two independent systems. One of these produces the hormones that maintain sexual desire in the bull. The other system produces the sperms that fertilise the eggs produced by the ovary in the female and also produces the hormones responsible for secondary male characteristics.

The sperms accumulate in the tortuous ducts which lie on the back of the testicle and which eventually lead from the testicle to the prostrate and seminal vesicles (the secondary secretory glands). At the moment of service they are diluted by nutrient fluids poured out by these glands. The actual dilution as well as the fluids themselves activate the sperms, and the mixture so formed is carried to the penis and thus implanted in the cow.

Experience with AI has taught us that fertility in the bull is very closely bound up with the quality of the semen produced. It should:

(a) Be adequate in volume.

(b) Contain an adequate number of sperms per unit of volume.

(c) Contain sperms that are highly active and have a good length of life.

(d) Be uniform in composition, with a minimum number of distorted forms of sperms.

These qualities can be influenced to a considerable degree by the management and feeding of the bull.

LESSONS FROM AI

Nevertheless defects are now known to exist which are hereditary in nature. These and other abnormalities, of which there are unfortunately a great many, can only be confirmed satisfactorily by careful semen tests.

As a result of the expansion of AI a great deal of knowledge has now accumulated which makes it possible to assess semen quality with greater accuracy. The owner of any bull which does not seem to be up to standard would be well advised to call in, through his own veterinary surgeon, the services of a specialist officer to make an investigation.

Many criticisms have been levelled at artificial insemination, but it can now be confidently stated that such a procedure, if carried out correctly, has many advantages.

The conception rates reported from most AI centres show figures little, if at all, below those for normal matings. AI can be used as a means of combating disease, avoiding the risk of spreading by the bull; it can be used to overcome anatomical defects; it is not so dependent on the time factor as natural service – a cow can be successfully inseminated up to 12 or more hours after she has gone off heat and would not accept the bull.

Further, through AI, bulls of high quality can be selected; and now that deep-freeze methods are being employed the bull of preference can often be stated. A number of perfectly normal animals have already been bred from semen stored at temperatures in the region of minus 21·1°C for well over a year, and as yet it appears that no limit can be set to the length of time for which semen so stored will survive.

Nevertheless constructive breeding in many herds still largely depends on natural service, and the success of that hinges very much on management when the bull becomes mature.

AGE TO START SERVING

To put a young bull in full service immediately he reaches ten or twelve months of age is to risk permanently impairing his fertility. I recommend that he should not be used at all until he is twelve months old and that, even then, he should be gently worked into full performance.

Controlled mating is preferable to letting a young bull run with heifers, otherwise he may serve an excessive number of times and do himself serious damage.

One service a week for the first six months of his working life should be your rule. This can be increased to two services a week during the next six months. Afterwards you can consider three times a week a safe figure.

MANAGING
THE
BULL

Above: Well-planned bull pen giving view of cows in yards.

Below: Methods of tethering bulls.

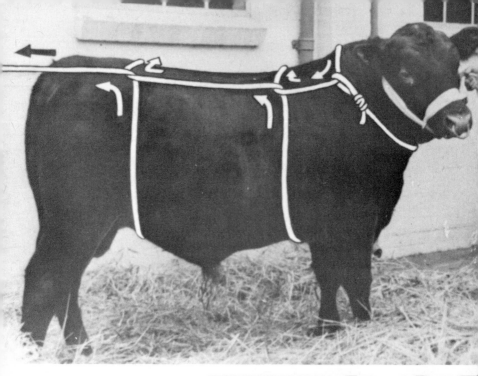

Top picture shows method of roping an animal to cast it for veterinary attention or foot treatment. Tension on the free end of the rope will cast the animal.

Right, farm-built stocks for confining an animal (with canvas hoist to take its weight) particularly useful for foot trimming. See constructional diagram, page 116.

A foot-bath for the dairy herd prevents many foot troubles. This one shown above can be drained and cleaned effectively (note bung in side wall); when it is not required, the cows will by-pass it if the main gate is open.

A breeding chart such as this can be fixed on the parlour wall or in the farm office and will provide at-a-glance details of how long each animal has been calved, when it is due for service, when it was confirmed in calf, when it should be dried off and steamed up, etc. Each cow is represented by a numbered magnetic cube.

Now I know that it is easy to put down such advice on paper but not so easy to keep to it in practice. There are times when it is important to get several animals served at about the same time. Further, there are times when you may be particularly anxious about getting a certain animal – perhaps a "shy" breeder – in calf and would like her to be served two or three times as an insurance.

Even so, I would set the upper limit for your bull at four services a week. That would be heavy work for a mature bull, but he should be able to stand it for several months provided he is well fed and properly handled and provided he gets a good rest after such a spell. Such a practice has now become routine at all AI centres, *i.e.* heavy work alternating with spells of rest.

SERVICES PER COW

As regards allowing more than one service per cow, it is certainly right to do so after the bull has been rested for some time. In such a case the semen ejaculated at the first service may not be sufficiently virile.

But when the bull is in regular use the quality of successive samples up to three services is more uniform, and thus it may pay on occasion to allow a second and even a third service where you have reason to think it might help to ensure conception.

But you should have regard for what further calls are likely to be made on the bull in the following days. If he is in heavy use, such excessive serving would be unwise.

BEST TIME OF SERVICE

This leads us to a consideration of the best time of service in relation to the heat period of the cow.

You will recall the explanation of how the eggs are shed from the ovaries and the point I made that an egg is not released from the ovary until after the cow has gone off heat. This actually takes place about 12 to 14 hours after the end of the heat period.

But then the egg has to travel down the fallopian tube before it gets to the tip of one of the uterine horns, and that journey takes roughly six hours.

Thus, if you have a cow served when she first displays signs of heat, the sperms may have to remain within the cow for 30 hours or more before they encounter the egg at the head of the uterine horn. Though many may survive this length of time, their activity tends to fall off fairly quickly, and there is a risk that conception will not take place.

It is obvious, therefore, that service in the latter stages of heat is more likely to result in conception for the simple reason that the sperms should be more virile when they meet the egg.

At the same time I must make the point that service too near the end of the heat period is not so effective as a little earlier, possibly due to some change in the nature of the vaginal secretions. These may become somewhat less beneficial to sperms. In the case of a ten-hour heat period I would advise service before the end of the ninth hour.

That again is paper advice and not so easy to put into practice,

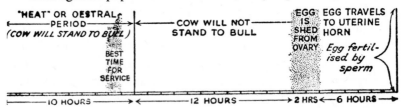

but if the general principle (which is diagrammatically illustrated here) is accepted as a background to the action you take at each service, it will guide you towards getting the best results.

SERVICE AFTER CALVING

Just two more points to make here. The first is that many dairy farmers and stockmen think that a mating at the cow's first heat period after calving is more likely to be successful than mating at subsequent heats.

This is not borne out by records. Indeed, these show that conception is more likely if service takes place as soon as possible after the third heat period, which is about 60 days following calving.

If, however, animals are left unduly long without being served it does appear to be increasingly difficult to get them into calf. This may in part be associated with the natural tendency to put on fat.

WHAT DETERMINES SEX

The second point is that the cow, contrary to what many people believe, is unable to influence the sex of her offspring. But the sperms of the bull are different; some carry the male chromosomes, others the female chromosomes – and so far as we know to date it is a matter of chance as to which type of sperm unites with the ovum from the cow.

Many farmers claim that their bulls throw calves of only one sex or are predominant in respect of one. A situation such as this is not uncommon and suggests that perhaps at some stage during mating, conditions are better for one kind of sperm. Research is now proceeding with a view to differentiating the male from the female sperms.

However, taken over a large number of calvings, the sexes tend to equalise.

AVOID PAIN AND FRUSTRATION

Now there are a few points to watch in connection with the procedure of service.

Here, it should be your principal object to see that the bull suffers no hurt and is not frustrated in any way when he is about to serve. Pain or frustration, particularly if it occurs with any regularity, may put the bull off permanently.

If you have provided a service pen or intend to build one, see that it has no dangerous edges or projections. Whether service takes place in a pen or yard, the floor should be sufficiently smooth (although with a non-slip finish) and have no gravel or stones lying about on which the bull may hurt his feet.

A load of sand spread thickly over the floor is a simple means of reducing the risks of slipping.

And do study the bull's preferences and idiosyncrasies. If he likes to spend a little time nosing around or making up his mind, then let him. Prodding and goading may easily set up that sense of frustration which must at all costs be avoided.

You may find, for instance, that he has a dislike for a particular yard or pen but will serve perfectly satisfactorily when allowed to do so in another place. Perfectly normal bulls have been known to refuse to serve altogether on strange premises, but behave normally when brought back to their familiar haunts.

It is an advantage to make a practice of observing a bull's routine, for then you can more quickly spot any slowing-up of sexual activity.

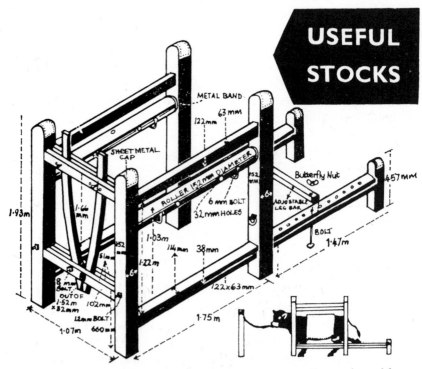

USEFUL STOCKS

These can-be-made-on-the-farm stocks are for foot-trimming. They can be used for bulls or cows. Small picture shows method of confining animal to deal with hind feet. Front feet can be trimmed in usual way while animal is secured.

This is more important than it sounds. It may lead to your being able to call veterinary advice before irreparable damage is done.

Several possibilities serve to illustrate this point. A bull may have suffered a back injury, there may be warts on the penis, he may have a piece of wire in his stomach or he may suffer from a foot injury.

There could be a *C. pyogenes* infection of the epididymis, prostrate and seminal vesicles, leading to inflammation of the urethra; there may be inflammation of the penis, arising from trichomoniasis infection; or the mucous membranes of the sheath and penis may adhere as a result of an injury by rubbing, as sometimes happens at an over-vigorous service. Again an injury may lead to abscess formation or a blood tumour known as a haematoma.

Any of these would cause the bull pain at service, possibly not enough at first to make him refuse to serve but at least sufficient to make his hesitancy noticeable. If you act on that signal, an examination can be made to find the exact cause and you can put matters right before the bull becomes infertile.

Similarly it would be wise to call in advice if you observe an abscess forming near the testicles. Immediate treatment is advisable.

Sometimes stones may form in the kidneys or bladder and be passed in the urine at irregular intervals, causing considerable pain.

Again immediate treatment is advisable.

FOOT TRIMMING

Then there is the matter of foot trimming. Do give this regular attention, and watch particularly for any tendency to walk lamely. It may be that the hoof has been worn unevenly or there is much adventitious growth on the sole. This must be removed and can only be done properly by throwing the bull or confining him in stocks. Nevertheless it is an essential job and needs to be done regularly if the bull does not get adequate exercise on hard ground.

117

The influence of feeding on the fertility of the bull must also be considered. It isn't enough just to bring him up well and then let him "make do" on anything that is available – some old

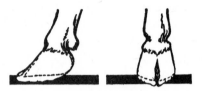

These front and side views of a bull's foot show, by the dotted line, just how it should be trimmed. Cows' feet should be regularly trimmed in the same way.

hay that the cows won't eat for example. He needs good feeding all the time.

This should be planned with some care. It's no use over-feeding with roughages alone; that will only make the bull pot-bellied and slothful and is just as bad as under-feeding.

BASIC AND PRODUCTION RATION

Give a basic ration of good green hay — about 1 lb (454 g) a day for each 100 lb (453 kg) of the bull's weight — and at least an equal amount of greenstuff, kale, cabbage, or silage, to provide vitamins.

On top of this you should give during the season that he is in use from 5 lb to 7 lb (2·26 to 3·17 kg) of concentrates a day, the ration having 17 per cent protein and a starch equivalent of approximately 68 per cent.

During spring and early summer, when many bulls are not normally in use, grazing or feeding with cut grass, clover, or lucerne should provide a sufficient ration, but do not leave it too late into the summer before you start giving a small ration of concentrates again. After the end of June grass soon loses its spring qualities.

BAD FEEDING AND INFERTILITY

This question of the standard of feeding is important. A bull can be put on a defective diet and it may be a year or more before any decline in fertility is even suspected. Yet, by that time, the damage to the bull may be advanced; changes could have taken place in the testicles that could not be put right.

A lack of vitamin A could do this. If you have any reason to feel that you are not able to give your bull a sufficiently nutritive diet at any time, you can, as a safeguard, sprinkle some synthetic vitamin A and D supplement on his concentrates once a month. Endeavour, however, to provide him with a complete, natural diet.

In cases where the bull has already been badly managed and is not up to standard you could fortify his ration for a few weeks by the addition of 5 to 7 per cent of good quality fishmeal or meat-and-bone meal plus a vitamin supplement – and increase his hay.

Alternatively a mixture of $\frac{1}{2}$ lb (227 g) each of fishmeal and dried grass meal added to a ration of hay, roots and oats will step up the protein and vitamin A content of the bull's ration.

As a last word on the subject of feeding and management I urge you to consider the many advantages of tethering. It provides the bull not only with a bite of grass that he can cut for himself, but with a health-giving exposure to sun and air and what must be a welcome opportunity to see some fresh surroundings.

From the foregoing you will see why I began by saying that the control of fertility in the bull is largely a farm job. There are so many ways in which you can make or mar a bull through feeding and management.

INFERTILITY TREATMENTS

Nevertheless there are, of course, cases of infertility that arise from other causes. Sometimes these are profound, but the knowledge gained through AI experience is greatly helping the research worker to determine the cause of any abnormality and gauge the possibilities of putting it right.

Some bulls may display a lack of sexual desire due to a lack of the appropriate hormone. This can sometimes be corrected by the injection of the right preparation.

An older bull that displays lack of desire may suffer from the fact that the hormone-secreting tissue in the testicles is wearing out – a condition which your veterinary surgeon may be able to postpone. For this purpose injections of pregnant mare's serum have had some success.

These and similar conditions can only be determined by a veterinary surgeon after a careful consideration of history and performance, satisfying himself as to the abnormality by a clinical examination and a study of a series of semen samples.

That is the vet's job. Yours is to rear, maintain and manage your bull well. Then he is less likely ever to need veterinary examination.

CHAPTER VIII

TACKLING ABORTION

THIS is an appropriate stage to discuss the question of abortion. I will deal with its possible causes and tell you what you can do in each case to reduce the risk in your herd.

But first let me make the point that a clear-cut distinction cannot be drawn to enable you to determine exactly what is a premature calf and one that has been aborted or "slipped."

Calves may be born prematurely some three or four weeks before full time and I should regard this as the rough dividing line; a calf produced earlier must undoubtedly be classed as an aborted calf. However, the argument is rather academic. Every calf born in any way abnormal or dead before full time should create concern and justifies investigation.

Contagious Abortion

Fortunately we now know how to control what was, until recently, a great dairy farming problem – contagious abortion.

This is caused by a germ, *Brucella abortus bovis*, that is usually picked up by cattle via the mouth – for example, by licking an aborted foetus or by eating grass or other fodder contaminated by discharge from an infected cow.

Once the germ gains access to a pregnant cow, it quickly makes its way to the womb and the cotyledons (buttons), there becoming firmly established, multiplying rapidly and setting up an insidious catarrh, leading in many cases to a separation of the membranes and an abortion.

It also creates later difficulties in getting the cow in calf again.

The dead foetus may be expelled at any time from four months onwards, but the greatest number of abortions from this cause occur between the fifth and seventh months of pregnancy.

Occasionally there may be some sign of an impending abortion; the lips of the vulva may be swollen and a little bloodstained discharge may be seen, but usually there is no warning and the dead calf will be found in a meadow or at the back of the standing.

Frequently the afterbirth remains in the cow. When it does start to come away, it will not be in one piece or even in large pieces, but in shreds. It is often yellowish-brown in colour with a slight sickly-sweet smell.

A bloodstained or yellowish discharge usually follows and may continue for three to six weeks. And all this time the cow is disseminating infection that other cows are likely to pick up.

METHODS OF CONTROL

Up to 1941 this disease ravaged our dairy herds and ruined many farmers. None of the popular "cures" – the billy goat, the donkey or the goose! – could keep it in check.

Then came the practice of inoculating bulling heifers with large doses of living and virulent bacteria. This was intended to help the animals build up a resistance. It seemed to reduce the number of abortions but, by the use of such a vaccine, the disease was actually being perpetuated and there was always the risk of calving troubles and infertility.

Another measure introduced was control by blood-testing and segregating all non-infected stock. Except where herds were self-contained and isolated this was never a practical proposition however.

But we are now in the happy position of having, in S 19, a highly satisfactory, reliable and safe vaccine against contagious abortion. This vaccine, while still alive and capable of stimulating a resistance to the disease, has no power to set up infection and so produce abortions (see reference to free vaccination scheme in chapter V). Whether you have a dairy herd or a beef herd, or a rearing herd, you can now take advantage of the Ministry of Agriculture's free vaccination scheme and have your young calves vaccinated.

One vaccination gives maximum protection over many years, but the immunity can still break down in the face of a severe challenge, *e.g.* the introduction of carrier animals into a clean herd.

This situation is most likely to arise when herds are being reconstituted from a variety of sources. It is a great disadvantage that there is no legal restriction to the sale of reactor (carrier) animals.

Just a point here to those farmers who are members of breed societies.

Some societies have strict regulations about vaccinations. They require blood tests to be taken before the vaccinations are carried out on stock other than calves.

It is wise to get the detailed information about this from your society; if you fail to meet the regulations you may be prevented from entering stock at official sales.

IF ABORTION OCCURS

Now let us consider the case of an outbreak of contagious abortion in a herd that is not vaccinated. Whilst, in the past, outbreaks of this disease were often associated with the introduction of a fresh batch of in-calf heifers, today infection may result from contamination of pastures by a foetus being dragged across it by foxes or dogs.

What should the farmer do who finds that one of his cows has aborted?

ISOLATE THE COW

Prompt action should be taken and the cow isolated. But before moving her, cut off any hanging cleansing – leaving about two feet. Swab the latter and the escutcheon with a suitable disinfectant. This will reduce the spread of infection in transit. Contaminated ground should be sprayed with carbolic and areas where the foetus, afterbirth and discharges have been should be covered with sacks soaked in the same.

Afterbirths and discharges should preferably be burned; where that is impractical they should be buried either deep in a dung heap or well down in the soil, preferably in an arable field rather than a stock pasture. Burying in a dung heap will only be suitable if the heap is a large one and has developed a considerable temperature internally.

The foetus and a piece of fresh afterbirth with cotyledons (the buttons) should be sent immediately in a water-tight container to the nearest veterinary laboratory for examination. The abortion may not be due to brucella organisms but to some other agent. Future action will depend upon the diagnosis.

Isolation should continue until all discharges have ceased which will be about six weeks.

If the abortion has occurred indoors shut the building up for 24 hours. Then scrape the bedding together and either burn it where it is or remove it and burn it. Scrape the walls, thoroughly cleaning them with more soda solution, then wash the premises out with a fresh disinfectant solution.

This will ensure that all infective material is destroyed and will enable you to use the premises again with confidence.

As a further precaution – I strongly advise this even if the blood tests prove negative – have all the empty animals vaccinated and adopt routine vaccination as part of your herd management.

In conditions of extreme urgency it may be necessary to vaccinate the in-calf animals with S45/20. Abortions which follow will almost certainly be due to any natural infection which existed before; the vaccine should not be blamed.

VACCINATION AND FERTILITY

There is a feeling that vaccination can have detrimental effects on the fertility of heifers and cows but, so far, research workers have been unable to find any evidence to support this belief. Even if isolated cases could be found they would hardly weigh against the great benefit that dairy farmers gain from using S 19. S45/20 vaccine can be used in adult stock in appropriate circumstances.

I do urge you to persist with the vaccination routine appropriate to your circumstances and not to drop it after a few years free of trouble. You may feel that having controlled the disease for some time, it is fairly reasonable to give up the vaccination.

That would be a most unwise step, for you would lay the incoming heifers open to infection and may find yourself faced with a heavy financial loss. This has already happened in some cases, and contagious abortion has crept back into herds.

Contrary to what used to be believed, the bull does not play a very large part in transmitting the disease although he may well do so if he serves an infected cow and a healthy one on the same day. No cows which have aborted should be served at least within six weeks of such an event and never whilst they are still discharging.

Bulls should not be vaccinated.

BLOOD AGGLUTINATION TEST

Cows and heifers that are vaccinated will react to the blood agglutination test. The strength of reaction is not so strong in the young subject and, moreover, tends to fade more rapidly than it does in the older animals.

The presence of agglutinins in the blood after vaccination makes it difficult to decide whether an animal has contracted a natural infection or not; but there are two ways of ascertaining this.

One is to take two or three blood tests at intervals of three or four weeks. The strength of the reaction will tend to rise rapidly in a naturally-infected animal; but where the reaction is due to vaccination carried out several months previously it will probably remain fairly constant over the tests or get weaker.

Agglutinins – the minute bodies in the blood which are estimated when a blood test is carried out – may also be present in the milk when an animal is naturally infected. Indeed, an increasing number of cases of human infection with *brucella abortus bovis* are reported each year; they arise through people drinking unpasteurised milk. But as the number of affected cows is getting less this menace to humans is being reduced.

In a small number of cases a closely related organism known as *Brucella melitensis* (the cause of Malta fever in goats) has been identified in cattle. Both this and *Brucella abortus bovis* produce a characteristic series of symptoms in humans associated with painful joints, headaches, sweating and fluctuating or undulating temperatures. Because of the latter characteristic the disease used to be described as undulent fever, but now all cases are classified under the heading of brucellosis. Fortunately the distribution of *Brucella melitensis* is very limited and there is no evidence that it is tending to spread.

DETECTING CARRIER COWS

In an effort to detect the carrier cows which are shedding the bacteria in their milk the ring test, in conjunction with the guinea pig inoculation test, has proved of considerable value.

Samples of milk are taken from their individual quarters and shaken up with a concentrated stained suspension of the organism *brucella abortus*. If agglutinins are present in the milk, they will cause the organisms to clump and be carried up to the top of the milk in the tube. After a few hours' incubation at body temperature a striking blue or pink ring, according to the dye used, will be seen on the top of the liquid in the tube.

THE BRUCELLOSIS (ACCREDITED HERDS) SCHEME

Since this scheme was introduced great progress has been made. It was an attempt to identify those herds which were free from infection and to enable lightly infected herds to qualify without too great an expenditure. More recently with the area application of compulsory slaughter of reactors, some areas have been cleared. Full details of this scheme can be secured from your Divisional Veterinary Officer.

Vibrio Foetus Infection (Vibriosis)

With contagious abortion now well under control other causes of abortion have been brought into prominence.

Perhaps the major one of these is vibriosis – named after the small spiral-shaped organism *vibrio foetus* which causes it in both cattle and sheep.

Vibrio foetus is not only a cause of abortion but is responsible for much infertility and poor conception rates.

The characteristic symptom of infection is a difficulty in getting animals in calf – often after repeated services or after several months of showing no sign of heat and being reckoned as in calf.

The disease is passed on only at the time of service and is brought on to the farm either by the purchase of an infected bull or by the introduction of an infected cow which the bull serves. Subsequently he will pass the infection on to other females.

KEY TO CONTROL

This gives us the key to control.

A clean herd can be kept clean if it is entirely self-contained or, when animals have to be purchased, if purchases are restricted to virgin heifers and to young bulls which have never previously been used.

If older bulls and cows have to be purchased, then it is wise to insist on a veterinary surgeon certifying them as free from the disease before the purchase is completed.

Where infection enters a herd its first effect is most likely to be a marked lowering of the conception rates. But if it is allowed to run its course then, in time, there may be a gradual return to normal as a herd immunity is built up sooner or later. This may show itself by an improved or normal conception rate in the adult herd whilst the heifers, with no immunity, are turning three or four times to the same bull.

It has been known for the disease to run its course quite

quickly. However, it is no use relying on that. For one thing – although it is now possible to treat an infected bull with a reasonable degree of success – the bull may possibly remain permanently infected and when he is used on heifers and on purchased cows he will transmit the disease to them, thus creating a continual problem of abortions and infertility.

BREEDING A CLEAN HERD

Therefore, where infection has gained a hold, the best thing to do is to plan immediately for its eradication by bringing into service a home-bred or purchased virgin bull and to use him exclusively on virgin heifers and on any cows which have been examined and found free of the disease.

In this way a clean herd will be gradually bred.

The older and infected bull – if he cannot be cured – can still be used on infected stock; and indeed all the stock can mix freely together so long as breeding is controlled in this way. It would, however, be wise temporarily to isolate any aborting animals.

The injection of mixed antibiotics is, however, giving good results.

Yet another alternative is to change over to AI, either entirely or for the virgin heifers and non-infected cows only.

But, in any case, you will need to work closely with your veterinary surgeon in eliminating the trouble arising from this disease, not only for diagnosis, but for clearing up obstinate cases of infertility.

FINDING INFECTED STOCK

There is no blood test whereby this disease can be identified, but a mucus agglutination test has proved of extreme value in detecting its presence. The agglutinins are to be found in the vaginal mucus, and the test is best made between heat periods because at the time of heat the cervix is open and the agglutinins seem to be greatly diluted by the increased flow of mucus; they are not then so easily detected.

The only way to determine whether a bull is affected or not

With this 8-stall 8-unit Carousel rotary milking parlour one man can milk single-handed at the rate of 85 cows per hour. The platform is geared by a 1 hp (0·75kW) electric motor. The operator lets in a cow by means of a cord-operated entry gate, identifies her, issues feed, washes udder, puts cups on and allows the platform to make its 15-second journey round until the next stall is alongside the entry gate, and so on, until the parlour is filled.

A farmer-designed tandem. All the entry and exit gates open and close pneumatically on a preset time-controlled sequence. In case of mishap, the cowman can override the automatic controls.

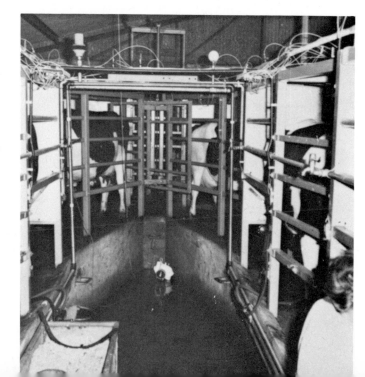

An intake of minerals in the correct proportions is necessary for the health and production of all animals. There is no harm in offering salt licks with calcium and phosphorus and traces of iodine, iron or cobalt. These are appetising, but the minerals should be in the concentrated foods supplemented by natural minerals in the pasture, silage and roughages.

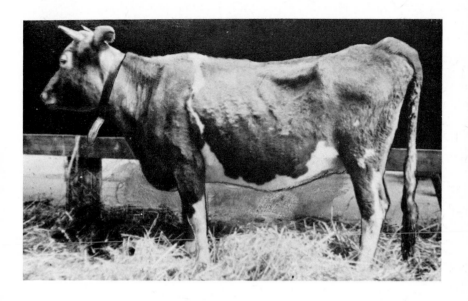

Cow above is in an advanced state
of Johne's disease. The characteristic symptom is the bubbly
dung pictured below.

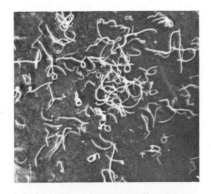

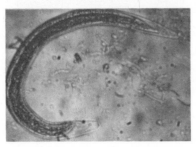

Top picture shows characteristic attitude of animal infected with husk—stretched out neck, continual coughing. Small pictures show lung worms responsible ($\frac{1}{4}$ actual size), and larval stage magnified approx. 500 times.

is to test-mate him with half-a-dozen virgin heifers. Should he be normal he will probably get them all in calf with less than two or three services; but if he is infected the average number of services required may be six or more.

This is a procedure which is being widely used at AI centres to ensure freedom from infection and the safety of their clients' herds.

Trichomoniasis

Now we come to another cause of abortion – trichomoniasis (first identified in 1936 in Hampshire), which from time to time and in certain localities may cause serious trouble. This, like *vibrio foetus* infection, is a true venereal disease.

It is caused by a microscopic parasite, rather like a minute tadpole, that lives in the womb and in the genital organs of the bull. It has been spread considerably through the agency of communal bulls, and the decline in the number of such bulls since the advent of AI is, therefore, particularly welcome.

CHIEF SYMPTOMS

The chief symptom of this disease is an early abortion. Sometimes the aborted foetuses are so small that they are not seen, especially if they are dropped out in the fields.

You should be particularly suspicious of this disease if you find cows that you thought to be safely in calf coming into season from nine to sixteen weeks after service. Yellowish-green thin discharges occurring each time the animals are bulling are an additional warning that trichomoniasis infection may be present.

In such circumstances it is best to consult your veterinary surgeon who will examine the discharges and determine if trichomoniasis is the cause. He will probably also examine the bull to see if he is infected, irrigating the sheath canal with a saline solution which should then be sent to a laboratory for examination.

METHODS OF TREATMENT

In the event of the bull proving to be infected it may be

necessary to have him cast and the genital apparatus thoroughly inspected and treated under an anaesthetic (as for vibrio infection) in the hope of being able to save him.

Cows are however more easy to treat and respond quickly to a course of womb irrigation and can be subsequently got in calf again.

If you can make use of an AI service while the disease is being tackled, I strongly advise you to do so. In this way you will eliminate any risk of infecting other bulls while the cows are being treated and you will also prevent further cows from becoming infected.

Mycotic Abortion

Apart from the secondary effects of a fever due to bacteria or viruses, in salmonellosis, for instance, and in fog fever, an appreciable number of isolated abortions can be attributed to fungi which are passed via the blood-stream to the uterus. Such species as aspergillus, mucor, and absidia are now known for certain to be associated with abortions, and since the extensive use of S.19 which has dramatically reduced the abortion rate due to brucella, by far the greater number of abortions in most parts of the country appear to be associated with one or other of the above fungi. Once again the importance of an accurate diagnosis is emphasised.

This type of abortion is quite closely related to the weather conditions prevailing during hay-making. The fungal spores develop to a large extent in wet hay and so eventually cause abortion after being fed over a period in the autumn and winter to dairy stock. The moisture content at the time of baling appears to be critical. Abortion may also be caused by salmonella and leptospira. A careful laboratory diagnosis should always be made.

Leptospiral Abortion

Abortions due to members of the group *L. hebdomadis* have now been reported in 30-40 per cent of herds. The parasite is carried in the kidneys of cows and is spread via the urine. It can be identified in foetal material and may cause severe mastitis; it is eliminated in the milk and can cause illness in humans. In pregnant cows there is early embryonic death, and full-time, small mummified foetuses are aborted with no clinical symptoms. The abortion rate may reach 10 per cent but is more severe in newly constituted herds. A good immunity soon builds up, and a good measure of control can be brought about by exposing bulling heifers to the infection. Cases usually occur in the summer when cows are out grazing. The parasite survives well in damp, wet areas which become contaminated by urine of cows and rodents.

Serious infertility can arise as the result of infection by the much rarer parasite *L. pomona.*

Ergot

This parasite – which affects ryegrass in particular but also other grasses such as Yorkshire fog, cocksfoot, etc – grows from spores in the soil which, after germinating, produce further spores which are spread by the wind and come to rest in the flowering heads of grasses.

The result is the development of a small, black, bean-shaped pod varying in size from one-eighth to one-half an inch (3 to 13 mm).

Such pods contain medicinal principles such as ergometrine which have the property of constricting involuntary muscle fibres. The womb contains a high proportion of this type of muscle tissue which may well be influenced by the presence of the active principles of ergot, to the extent that contraction and a premature birth occurs. However, in cattle ergot poisoning is more commonly associated with necrosis of the ends of the limbs where rings of dead tissue may form (in humans St. Anthony's Fire).

Grasses can be seen to be infected when the flowers are ripening – from early summer to autumn – and a very heavy infestation encourages a diagnosis of ergot poisoning. It is also possible that the ergot beans may be present in contaminated grain, particularly barley in some years.

Too Much Kale

There is also the possibility that, during winter, feeding excessive quantities of kale may affect the cows' ability to assimilate the minute but necessary amount of iodine that they need and so cause abortion.

The exact requirements of iodine under all circumstances are not known but, whilst there are few areas in Great Britain where a deficiency is likely to occur, absorption may be interfered with by an excess of calcium in the diet. This may be avoided by the regular use of iodised mineral supplement or licks.

Lack of Green Foods

Under abnormal circumstances a deficiency in vitamin A may lead to abortion. The greatest risk of this is with cows that are housed for long periods without having in their rations some carotene-rich foods such as green hay, silage, kale or dried grass.

Similarly, cows that go through a long dry summer on burnt-up pastures without an adequate supplement of green food may lack vitamin A. The measures that you can take against both of these risks are obvious.

Mechanical Causes

Finally, it is necessary to deal with abortions arising from mechanical causes.

I think we can quite definitely rule out some of the farm "theories" in this respect. Aeroplanes flying low over the fields are not likely causes of abortion. Our war experience taught us that. Even when bombs fell in fields and killed a number of animals, abortions in those not hit were extremely rare.

Direct injuries such as an attack by a horse or a severe horning by another cow are far more likely causes of abortion than shock or fright.

[For further causes of abortion see also Salmonellosis and Fog Fever.

CHAPTER IX

PRODUCTION DISEASES

(*Metabolic Disorders*)

IN the chapters dealing with infertility and abortion I referred to the importance of maintaining the finer "balances" in feeding. Now we can go a little further and consider how an "imbalance" or lack of balance can, in fact, cause disease and how we can discover such conditions.

The term *disease* applied in this context may seem unusual for it does not apply to the presence of known disease-producing agents, but the process nevertheless is a pathological one. Problems arise through the increased stress of production; the machine, so to speak, runs out of ingredients because of the sudden heavy demand put upon it at calving time, for example, when milk production starts. Another example is hypomagnesaemia (grass or lactation tetany) which occurs when animals are turned out to pasture in the spring. It may also happen that continuous, though less severe, demands are put upon the animal and reserves are depleted. This could lead to a metabolic disorder such as occurs in ketosis.

The input-output balance of nutrients is never static but varies within known limits under standard circumstances. Much can be learned as to the status of the herd by providing what is called a metabolic profile (see illustration below). Blood samples of an appropriate number of animals are taken and a chemical analysis of selected nutrients carried out. An investigation of this kind can bring to light a variety of situations such as:

1. Chronic shortage of drinking water.
2. Deficiency in carbohydrate intake, especially in high-yielding dairy cows.
3. Evidence of sodium deficiency.
4. Problems connected with high levels of fertilisation of pasture.
5. Various mineral imbalances associated with the unusual and complex problem known as *parturient paresis*.
6. Sub-clinical hypomagnesaemia in herds which results in hyper-irritability and a particularly severe form of parturient paresis especially in late autumn and winter.
7. A high incidence of hypo albuminaemia and anaemia, especially in late winter.
8. A deficiency of copper, especially in dry cows fed maintenance diet only. Most of these problems can be corrected by dietary adjustment.

Such problems may exist unknown to the farmer or there may be only a suspicion that something is wrong. But when the

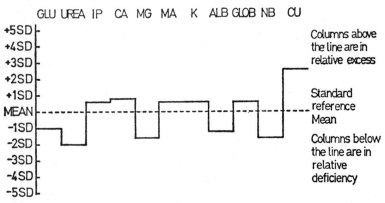

Profile histogram of a herd with excessive copper but low urea, magnesium and haemoglobin concentration.

SD = Standard deviation. More than one SD suggests that action should be taken.)

134

metabolic profile brings the defect to light appropriate action can be taken. Such tests may be carried out spasmodically, but to get the greatest benefit it may be desirable to have them done on a routine basis, say twice-yearly – once during the grazing season and 6-8 weeks after the winter feeding period has begun. Thus a serious breakdown associated with a number of the conditions involved here, could be avoided by permitting action to be taken in the initial stages of a deteriorating situation.

For the purposes of investigation the herd is divided into dry, middle and high-yielding animals – seven animals being sampled from each group (see illustration below). This allows for the state of productivity of the animals in relation to their feed intake within the particular group.

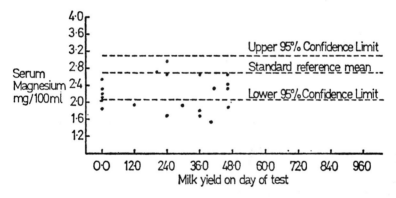

Scatter diagrams from same herd as previous illustration, showing high incidence of hypomagnesaemia. Twenty-one animals sampled, nine revealed Mg levels lower than the minimum confidence level.

The chemical analysis usually carried out includes glucose, urea, inorganic phosphorus, calcium, magnesium, sodium, potassium, albumin, globulin, haemaglobin and copper.

Whilst there is much to be learnt about the significance of the picture obtained, this procedure is already proving valuable as an early warning system, pinpointing likely deficiencies or excesses, and, as it were, monitoring the situation. Much care and experience is needed to interpret the results and factors such as time of year, prevailing weather conditions, changing food regimes etc. have to be taken into account.

Milk Fever

This common disease may present itself in a dramatic way. The affected cow is found down on her side – and possibly unconscious – with her head twisted round on to her side in a characteristic manner, almost as if there was a kink in the neck. If the neck is straightened out it will return to its twisted position on release.

When the disease has been met before it is not so alarming. For one thing you know what to look for. You should be particularly alert just before and just after calving – up to a week afterwards in fact – watching for signs of unrest.

Paddling with the hind feet, followed by a tendency to sway about rather dangerously, are distinctive symptoms in the early stages.

These symptoms are associated with a fall in the calcium level of the blood.

In good health this fluctuates within very narrow limits over the seasons, but a fall below the lowest limit is a serious matter. When this falls to approximately half its normal level the cow cannot stand.

I must emphasise that the disease is not due to a deficiency of calcium in the body but to a temporarily low calcium content of the blood. Apparently what happens is that there is a break-down in the animal's metabolism and it cannot withdraw from the bone-stores sufficient calcium quickly enough to balance the rapid drain caused through the secretion of colostrum and milk. Also appetite falls and calcium intake drops.

GLANDS MAY BE INVOLVED

We do not yet know the full facts. The parathyroid gland is involved as this controls calcium metabolism through the hormone it secretes, but a failure of this gland is not the basic cause of a calcium blood-level decline. Recent facts indicate that the adrenal gland may well play an important part in this complex by relaxing temporarily its stimulating effect upon the other hormone-producing glands. But the fall in blood calcium is not primarily the cause of the disease.

What we do know is that milk fever rarely occurs at the first calving, occasionally occurs at the second calving but is most common at the third, fourth and fifth calvings. Some cows will go down two or three times and need repeated treatment.

The most susceptible cows are high-yielders, especially those that are in good condition and have had an easy calving. Those that have a prolonged and difficult labour hardly ever develop the disease, probably because activity of the adrenal glands is maintained. In other words a shock or stimulus to the nervous system has a beneficial effect.

Cases suddenly crop up with a change in the weather for the worst. This could in part be due to a fall in the blood magnesium which is known to be influenced by adverse weather conditions. An excess or deficiency of magnesium or phosphorus can predispose to milk fever, and the diet may be unbalanced in these minerals when the weather changes.

TREATMENT

Immediately a cow goes down with milk fever she should be propped up on her brisket by means of trusses of hay or straw or sacks of cake or earth and her head held forward by tying a rope to the horns.

If recovery is prolonged, the cow should be turned over on her other side every two or three hours to prevent any risk of her becoming blown or cramped.

The modern method of treatment is well known. It involves giving an injection of a solution containing calcium borogluconate under the skin in the region of the shoulder and massaging the skin well so that it is thoroughly dispersed.

When an animal is semi-comatose it may be necessary also to inject directly into the jugular or milk vein to obtain a more speedy action.

This treatment has the effect of restoring the calcium level of the blood; once that has been done, the body seems able again to draw on its own reserves in the normal way and to maintain the blood level subsequently.

HELP HER TO RISE

If a treated cow appears to recover but does not make any attempt to get up, you can try various dodges – an electric goader, a dog or her calf, or shout in her ear – as persuasion. Help should be available to lift her from under the buttocks and to steady her as she gets to her feet hind legs first, pulling her tail as she tries to straighten her front legs.

Once the cow is up it may help if you let her see her calf. But do not let it suckle for at least twelve hours, at which time you can ease any quarter that the calf misses.

If you prefer not to bring the calf back to the cow, then wait twelve hours before easing her off and in any case don't milk her out completely for 48 hours.

See that feeding is moderate for about a week, giving hay and some bran mashes but no concentrates and no grass. Anything that stimulates milk production should be introduced gradually. To attempt to raise the cow's yield too quickly may cause a relapse.

OLD-FASHIONED REMEDY

The calcium borogluconate injection method, although hardly more effective than the old one of blowing up the udder with some form of pump, has the great advantage that it eliminates any handling of the udder and the use of teat syphons, thus considerably reducing the risk of mastitis infection.

But the surprising success achieved by blowing up the udder with air may well, in the light of modern enquiry, be significant.

One view is that the nerve endings in the distended udder are stimulated, having a favourable reflex effect upon the hormone system and presumably bringing the adrenal gland once more into play.

Another school of thought has interpreted its success to be

due to stopping the drain of milk salts – especially, of course, the minerals.

Some research workers believe that the drain of protein is of equal importance to that of the minerals and that it is a loss of this fraction which has such a serious effect.

PREVENTIVE ACTION

The injection of large doses of vitamin D prior to anticipated calving has now been replaced by a safer synthetic derivative. This helps to raise the blood-calcium level at this critical time and it can be aided by introducing a special calcium booster ration immediately after calving.

IMPORTANCE OF PROTEIN

And there is equal justification for including good quality animal protein in the steaming-up ration – at least 5 per cent of fishmeal or meat-and-bone meal. The drain on the animal's reserves via the calf and the udder is very appreciable during the last few weeks before calving. Use the standard dairy ration for steaming-up, but reduce the amount somewhat during the last week before calving.

As far as prevention is concerned the answer certainly does not lie in abandoning modern methods of steaming-up and milking before calving when this has to be done.

Some people blame these practices, but it is a fact that cows are affected with milk fever whether they are steamed up or not. Indeed, it can be argued that it is a good thing to milk the cow out gently before she calves rather than to let the milk come down with a rush and take it all away at once, so draining the system of some readily-available calcium.

Similarly, although it is a wise practice to provide an adequate intake of calcium through liming the soil on which the cow-crops are grown and by including a mineral mixture in the food, this, too, is no guarantee against milk fever.

TREAT THEM ROUGH!

The more drastic measure of letting cows calve outside on the pastures or at least in an open yard, may be tried when other measures have failed. In other words – treat them rough.

If any of the preventive measures referred to fail, the system of injecting calcium just before calving and immediately after calving should be adopted. Certain cows seem to be particularly susceptible and these are the ones which you will need to safeguard in this way.

You should also make it a normal practice, with all cows, to ease off their steaming-up ration during the few days before calving (and to put them on a bare pasture in spring) to give a laxative drench – 1 lb (454 g) black treacle in sufficient warm water to make a drench – just before calving, to stop pre-milking 24 hours before calving and not to milk out any cow completely for the first 72 hours after calving.

Observing these rules will help to keep milk fever cases down to a minimum.

Hypomagnesaemia
(Hereford Disease, Lactation Tetany or Grass Staggers)

The scientific name, hypomagnesaemia, is a good description of the disease as it is a condition of low blood magnesium. Since the earliest investigations were associated with an enterprising veterinary surgeon in Hereford it was initially given this name. To confuse the situation further, however, two other names are used (though less and less) which refer to certain aspects of the problem. Staggers and muscular tremors are by no means confined to animals in milk or necessarily at grass. The disease is however, not to be confused with "tetanus", though both diseases display muscular tremors, those of hypomagnesaemia being intermittent and involving the skin muscles, whilst in true tetanus the whole body is affected and is often in prolonged tension.

ALARMING SYMPTOMS

If the fall in magnesium is sudden and pronounced, it will produce alarming symptoms of excitement, and death may occur within a few minutes. A less marked fall causes an increased sensitivity with muscular tremors, a flickering of the eyelids and an increased excitability to local disturbances such as the presence of a stranger or a banging door.

The low-grade or chronic type of lactation tetany may persist for several weeks, resulting in a fall in condition and a considerable reduction in milk yield.

The response to magnesium injections is not so good as the response to calcium injections for milk fever. Magnesium is very slowly absorbed from the gut, and injections must be given slowly otherwise heart failure may occur.

Success has been claimed for various methods of providing magnesium in the food, but we still have many more cases in some years than in others. Further, while certain pastures – especially water meadows and the hay made from them – have been considered responsible, there is no consistent proof that this is so.

Whilst cases of hypomagnesaemia may be encountered at almost any time of the year, the great majority occur in the spring, shortly after dairy herds are turned out to grass.

The incidence in dry cattle and beef animals, however, reaches a peak during the colder months of the year when such stock is likely to be exposed to severe climatic conditions and be somewhat short of natural or artificial foods.

It has been shown that the balance of magnesium in the blood may be affected by sudden changes of temperature. There is a seasonal variation in the blood levels which is lowest in the early winter months; if, at this time, cattle are brought indoors the blood level may rise rapidly – and return to a lower level if such beasts are once more put outside.

Whilst the mechanism of control of blood magnesium is still not fully understood it appears to be influenced by the rapid intake of highly nitrogenous substances. Cattle turned out onto rich pastures which have been heavily dressed with sulphate of ammonia may quickly develop characteristic symptoms of lactation tetany, especially if the magnesium levels in the soil are low.

TREATING PASTURES

The application to the pastures of relatively small quantities of magnesium salts in the form of calcined magnesite (a commercial by-product containing over 90 per cent of magnesium oxide) has been shown to have a controlling influence on the disease. Six hundredweight of calcined magnesite per acre (753 kg/ha) will give beneficial effects so long as the ground to which it is applied is not too alkaline. In other words there is little advantage in dressing limey pastures. In other cases, however, the beneficial effect appears to be spread over 4-6 years.

When calcined magnesite is fed directly to animals during the critical periods of the year at the rate of 2 ounces (57 g) per animal per day, a good measure of prevention is assured, but as soon as this feeding is stopped the animals again become susceptible and, if still prone to the disease, will quickly develop symptoms, the blood magnesium level again falling accordingly.

This knowledge justifies the feeding of calcined magnesite or of magnesium-rich mineral supplements during the most dangerous parts of the year; but it is doubtful whether it is an economic proposition to encourage the use of magnesium salts at this high level in concentrate foods or in mineral mixtures right through the year. Seventy pounds (31·75 kg) of calcined magnesite added to the ton of food will provide 2 oz per 4 lb (57 g per 1·81 kg) of mixture.

Because of the difficulty of anticipating the occurrence of the disease, there is a natural tendency to feed the supplement over extended periods. This, however, is unwise and may lead to an upset in the calcium metabolism, and in young animals symptoms of rickets may appear. The supplement could safely be taken out during July, August and early September.

A rough and ready way to give protection for short periods, especially in connection with beef animals out of doors, is to put a bag of calcined magnesite in the water trough and agitate gently once a day to encourage diffusion. A new system is now available whereby controlled amounts of soluble sodium acetate can be added to the drinking water as required. Another very effective way is to dust the pastures with the very finely-ground powder at the rate of 56 lb an acre (62·77 kg/ha) This is held in the foliage and gives a good degree of protection for at least six weeks.

One useful means of providing a steady small supply of magnesium is the magnesium "bullet" which when pushed down the gullet comes to rest in the reticulum or second stomach. It does not supply the full daily requirement of the mineral but is a useful insurance, especially where intake is minimal.

Acetonaemia

Acetonaemia is another disease that arises from an unbalanced diet – although not directly connected with minerals as far as we know.

What happens in this disease is that the liver, which normally oxidizes fat with the aid of a number of substances but especially with the sugar from starchy foods, is unable to do this completely because of a shortage of the right sort of carbohydrates. Consequently fat accumulates in the liver.

The result of this is that certain breakdown products from the fat – ketones – are released into the blood stream. One of these in particular, called acetone, creates the sweet smell of the cow's breath and milk that is characteristic of the disease and gives rise to its other name: ketosis.

Other obvious symptoms are loss of appetite (she will pick over greenstuff but not concentrates), fall in milk yield and general depression.

Occasionally a more acute type of disease is encountered: the animal goes down as if suffering from milk fever and in such a case the distinction between acetonaemia and milk fever is the sweet smell of the milk and breath and the fact that acetonaemia usually occurs later than milk fever.

Powders can be obtained from veterinary chemists for testing either milk or urine for the presence of acetone. A colour reaction indicates existence of the disease.

Acetonaemia is most common in high-yielding herds (especially those with high butterfats) and seems to occur as lactation rises to its peak and towards the end of a long period of housing and particularly if the cows have been kept tied up day and night instead of being allowed free exercise.

It also appears to be associated with the question of roughage; high-yielding cows that are given a below-minimum ration of roughage to enable them to consume a full concentrate ration are prone to acetonaemia. The quality of the carbohydrates and the amount of non-protein nitrogen also seem to have a bearing on the development of the condition.

In one experiment in which animals in milk were receiving a standard ration containing 25 per cent protein almost every animal developed acetonaemia. A small percentage showed signs when the protein was 14 per cent and at the extreme of 9·5 per cent milk yield was depressed, but only one case occurred.

From these facts one thing is obvious; acetonaemia is something that we should try to prevent – on the farm.

METHODS OF PREVENTION

With low-yielding cows there should be no difficulty at all; a sound, well-balanced ration will keep the trouble away. But with high-yielders a little extra attention is necessary.

As a piece of general advice cows should be dried off in lean condition and not be steamed-up for more than 4-5 weeks. This is of course if they are heavy milkers. It should start at 2-4 lb (1-2 kg) of concentrate ration, working up to 8-10 lb (4-5 kg) before calving. The total protein of the production ration should be between 16 – 18 per cent. After calving the protein can be dropped to 10 – 12 per cent.

Finally, sudden changes should be avoided and regular exercise encouraged even if only in yards.

TREATMENT

With regard to treatment of acetonaemia, it should be prompt. Your vet will have his own treatment and should be consulted.

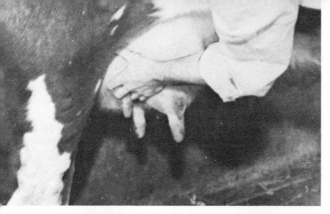

RECOGNITION

OF

MASTITIS

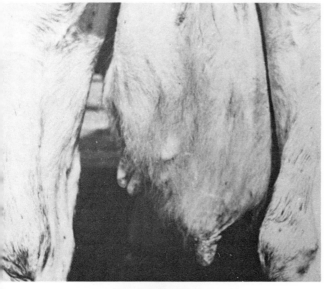

Above, the light quarter being handled has been affected with mastitis and now gives a reduced amount of milk. Centre, one side of this udder has completely dried up as a result of mastitis infection. Below, udder of a down-calving animal needs constant examination; signs of hardness and heat may indicate onset of summer mastitis.

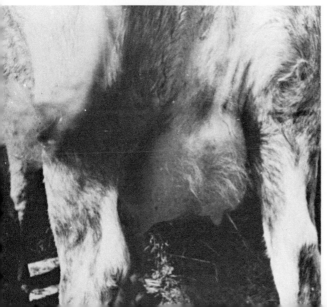

MASTITIS

Use of a strip-cup will show if mastitis is present. As soon as the tell-tale flecks are seen, immediate precautionary action should be taken.

Disposable paper towels are ideally suited for drying surplus water off the udder and, once again, reduce the risk of spreading infection.

After handling the udder of a cow, th hands should be thoroughly rinsed in d infectant. Rubber gloves are an added pr caution to preventing mastitis spread.

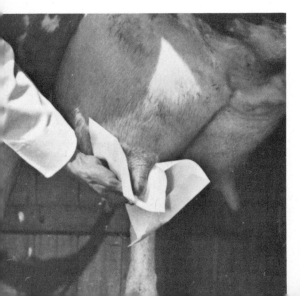

CONTROL

Washing cows' udders with warm water helps prevent the spread of infection from one cow to the other and is preferable to the use of a bucket of water shared between several animals.

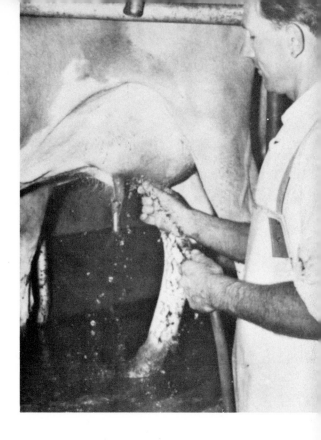

After milking, a final precaution is to dip each teat in an anti-bacterial solution. This is the most important action of the entire routine.

To safeguard the dried-off cow, as soon as its lactation ends each of its quarters should be infused with a suitable slow-release antibiotic preparation.

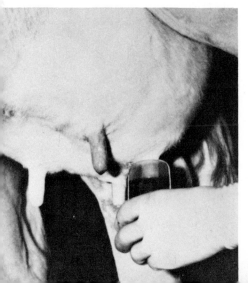
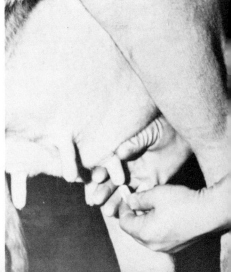

Cross-suckling is a vice which, if left unchecked, may lead to disease, particularly mastitis, in later life. An effective method of prevention is a nail-studded halter pictured below.

To cease milking for a day or two, only easing off the udder if necessary, will bring about appreciable relief in itself but there is no infallible remedy. Cutting out the concentrate ration for 2 to 3 days and feeding only crushed cereals will help recovery. This is virtually raising the starch equivalent (energy) and lowering the protein levels. Large amounts of kale and silage contribute to the latter course.

Glycerine by the mouth is sometimes satisfactory. It should be given in four half-pint (284 ml) doses over two days. Propylene glycol will act just as well as glycerine. Both are more effective than glucose since seven-eighths get through the rumen without being taken up by the bacteria. With glucose, only one-eighth gets through.

Some success has also been achieved by injections of glucose or of choline chloride – which only goes to show how complex the origin of this disease is likely to be.

It may be helpful in any case to give gentle exercise and tempt the affected animal with a warm mash containing bran, flaked maize, fishmeal and 2 ounces (57 g) of yeast; good quality carbohydrate, animal protein and the vitamin B in yeast have a stimulating effect on the fatty liver.

Other Metabolic Disorders

I have covered these three diseases in detail because they are the most common ones arising from mineral or metabolic disturbances. But they by no means end the list.

A deficiency in phosphorus may cause rickets, brittle bones, unthriftiness and even some degree of infertility; a deficiency in manganese may delay shedding of eggs from the female ovaries; a deficiency in iodine may interfere with the function of the thyroid gland which controls animal metabolism, and a shortage of either copper or cobalt will cause unthriftiness and poor growth in young stock.

How can we deal with these problems on the farm?

145

This brings us back again to good farming and good stockmanship.

Good farming in this sense means a proper use of phosphates, potash and, above all, lime. A lime deficiency will mean that crops cannot make the fullest use of phosphates and potash.

On the other hand, an excessive amount of lime may similarly result in supplies of copper, cobalt, manganese and iodine becoming "bound" in the soil so that crops cannot take them up.

As for good stockmanship, in this sense it means that you should use reasonable care in planning the cows' rations to ensure that, as far as possible, essential food ingredients are always being supplied. And the best way to do this is to give as much variety as possible.

It is by giving an excess of one particular food to the exclusion of several others that you may set up an "imbalance."

For example, excessive quantities of certain green foods, particularly the brassicas, may interfere with the thyroid gland function and lead to early abortions or full-time calves being born dead.

Similarly, to dispense entirely with concentrate feeding during spring and summer may lead to shortages of minerals. You may be able to get good daily yields from your grass, but this will not provide adequate minerals nor possibly enough starch. So a grass-balancer ration is essential for good health, milk production *and* fertility.

A great deal of study is now being given to the digestive disturbances that take place in the rumen or first stomach. This organ acts as an incubator in which literally billions of protozoa and bacteria are all the time breaking down the food materials swallowed by the cow.

It can be said with some truth that the life of the cow is dependent on their activities; yet they are themselves controlled to some extent by the physical and chemical nature of the foods provided.

The fibre is broken down by the protozoa, the breakdown products being taken up by bacteria which multiply in enormous numbers. They also take part in the synthesis of certain vitamins such as B_{12} and C, the former requiring a supply of cobalt in the food.

Bacterial activity in the rumen is important; the very health of the cow depends upon it and the bacteria must not be disturbed by any violent changes in the composition of the food – otherwise we can expect one or other of the numerous metabolic diseases to appear.

But we do have to recognise that, although under all normal conditions there is no substitute for proper husbandry of crops and stock, there are characteristic mineral deficiencies in certain areas.

A lack of cobalt on the moors of south-west England has in the past made large tracts uneconomic as grazing grounds, and in parts of East Anglia and in recently-claimed river valley lands in chalky areas the copper status of the soil appears to be extremely poor.

Where these natural deficiencies cannot be remedied by good husbandry the development of proprietary brands of special mineral mixtures is important.

Salt Deficiency (The Licking Syndrome)

Sodium deficiency is occurring with increasing frequency and seems to go hand in hand with the trend towards intensive grassland management.

The addition of nitrogen and potassium to pastures reduces the availability of sodium, so one would expect trouble soon after turning out to pasture. But cases also occur in winter when high-nitrogen silage is introduced ad lib.

A cow producing 22 lb (9·98 kg) of milk per day loses just under half an oz. (14 g) of sodium/potassium this way, as well as some in the excreta.

Where a deficiency arises appetite falls off, milk yield declines and an intense craving for salt is reflected in the development of a licking mania. Animals lick the coat and or legs of their companions, drink urine and investigate anything with a salty flavour. Severe cases of scouring may occur.

All commercially-mixed rations should contain adequate salt, but if this is not so the situation is soon remedied. If a shortage arises in the grazing season, however, grassland can be sprayed with 14 lb (6·35 kg) of common salt in 500 gallons of water per acre (2,273 kg/ha).

Hypocuprosis

On the other hand, conditions are encountered where the animal suffers from a mineral deficiency although there is sufficient in the pasture. This is especially true of copper, and the condition known as hypocuprosis has received considerable attention over the last few years.

A condition of unthriftiness associated with a copper deficiency was observed many years ago both in Australia and in the north of Scotland where stock-rearing was difficult because the animals would not grow satisfactorily. When treated with small doses of copper salts the victims rapidly returned to normal health and started to grow.

COPPER BECOMES UNAVAILABLE

In more recent times a similar problem has been encountered in various parts of England where in fact there was adequate copper in the soil but the animals could not utilise it. Successive generations of calves showed increasing inability to grow at the normal rate though suckling their dams and living out at grass.

Examination of blood samples of the dams and the calves in question revealed the almost complete absence of any copper reserves which would normally be located in the liver.

It would appear that where little or no concentrates are being fed to stock – and these always contain sufficient amounts of copper – the animals are unable to obtain their copper from grass and so suffer a progressive depletion.

The symptoms are best observed in calves of the black breeds. The hair becomes rusty-red in appearance and can be pulled off as though moth-eaten; the pigment fades out from around the eyes, giving a spectacled appearance.

Such a condition is much more widespread than is realised.

Young animals, in particular, need copper to maintain a normal rate of growth; if this falls to a very low level they remain stunted and unthrifty.

One gram of copper sulphate given as a drench per month is perfectly adequate to maintain growth. The reserves of the dam can be rectified by giving a slightly increased amount. But they will get none from roots and straw, and apparently none either from grass under certain circumstances.

Such a copper deficiency may also be induced and is encountered in certain parts of the country, being known in these parts as teart. This disease is dealt with more fully in chapter XIII.

Wherever there is evidence of a particular deficiency or need, the farmer should not hesitate to seek advice through his veterinary surgeon and then to use the appropriate mineral mixture or injection for his purpose.

Barley "Poisoning"

A suspicion has grown over the years that barley was in some way dangerous, especially when large quantities of the same year's harvest were used. We now know that up to 85 per cent can be used in some rations for beef cattle with perfect safety. There are some dangers, however, which must be watched for.

Firstly, there is the risk of over-feeding. If an animal has free access to barley and gorges itself the situation can be serious and lead to death. The rumen becomes distended and impacted with a dry, solid mass which reduces rumen movement and prevents the digestive juices from being mixed up with the contents.

The mass becomes acid and all the vitamin B-forming bacteria die. Lactic acid builds up and accumulates in the bloodstream. Normally this is kept at a low level by the presence of thiamine. But when this is no longer available, because the bacteria which produce it are put out of action, a severe acidosis occurs.

This is reflected in a black, smelly scour, breathing becomes difficult, and death may occur in 10-14 days if treatment is not introduced. One of the most effective measures is the injection of a vitamin B mixture into the bloodstream and under the skin.

Secondly, feeding barley which has been harvested wet and allowed to ferment in air produces intoxication due to the presence of alcohol, and there have been many cases associated with blindness, staggering and collapse. There may also be some diarrhoea in the early stages.

Finally, mouldy barley may also be highly dangerous as a feedingstuff (see under fog fever).

Liver Abscesses

The increase in liver abscesses reported in recent times has rightly or wrongly been associated with the introduction of new methods of feeding, such as the early-weaning system, and the inclusion of large quantities of barley in the ration. Some of the sharper siliceous parts of the barley grain can usually be found deeply embedded in the wall of the rumen. The tendency to build up acidity especially round the edge of the food mass and the reduced rate of movement of the food within the stomach tend to cause a clumping of the villi and damage the underlying tissues, thus allowing bacteria to penetrate into the bloodstream and so through to the liver. There is also undoubtedly liver damage which may predispose to the establishment of bacteria and the development of groups of firm rounded abscesses up to tennis ball in size, with thick creamy contents. Further work on this aspect is in progress.

CHAPTER X

MASTITIS
CONTROL AND TREATMENT

AT least three out of every four cases of mastitis ought never to happen. They should be prevented by proper routine methods on the farm.

In the early days of research on mastitis *Streptococcus agalactiae*, *dysgalactiae* and *uberis* dominated the scene because they were more susceptible to penicillin, but chemotherapy has so improved that almost none of the important organisms, e.g. staphylococci and *E. coli*, is now beyond treatment. However, the impact of all these can be greatly reduced by combining treatment with good hygiene and preventive methods.

Now this is important. It means that if you take sufficiently active steps on the farm you can avoid many mastitis cases – and save yourself a lot of worry and money.

ITS PREVENTION

So let us get down straight away to this vital job of prevention. What is the secret?

Well, we know that *S. agalactiae* is carried by many cows not obviously suffering from mastitis. We know that the germs are to be found inside the udder and in teat sores. We also know that they multiply in these places but do not do so away from these sources.

Knowing all this makes it natural to ask why there are not many more cases than do actually occur. And here the answer seems to be that some starting point is required – something that allows the germs to settle down and multiply in the udder tissues.

Although there may be certain physiological causes not yet clearly understood, very often the starting point is provided by an injury. In fact, it is common experience that when an udder is damaged by a kick, or is horned, or torn by barbed wire or trodden on, mastitis is often the sequel.

HOW MANY CASES OCCUR

But it is important to realise that the germs do not necessarily need a gross injury, such as one of those indicated, to gain access to the udder tissue. They can pass through a crack that is so often caused by some slight mis-handling of the udder.

Indeed, it is probably through the unseen abrasions of the delicate membrane linings of the teats and udder tissues that the bulk of mastitis cases develop. It is this kind of damage, which can so easily occur at the time of milking, against which you should guard.

Your first step in this direction should be to establish a standard milking technique, and stick to it.

Devise your routine to take advantage of the natural phenomenon of "let down" – and remember that this is conditioned by associations – the clanging of buckets, the smell of food or the massage applied before milking – and that any marked variation in the routine will interfere with the let-down process.

UNSEEN DAMAGE

Thus, if a cow holds back her milk, it is, ten to one, your fault and not hers. But the fact that she holds it back may lead to your tugging on the teat cups or weighting them or leaving the machine on for extra time – the very actions that should at all costs be avoided. The damage they do is unseen but very real. I particularly emphasise this. It is a proved fact that the quicker and easier the milk is removed, the less likely is injury to occur.

Don't take this to mean that I advise such dodges as increasing the vacuum pressure of your machine. I don't. Keep it constant, at the rates advised by the manufacturers. If you change it you will do the cows more harm than good.

You can, of course, increase the pulsations, but you should not raise the pressure on the suction pipe. Inadequate vacuum reserve with consequent surging is, however, important and to be avoided.

And do not think that you can reduce the milking time of your cows to a standard level. You can't. Each cow has her own time.

It's your job to get to know that time.

PROPER MILKING ROUTINE

Towards the end of it (it should average from $4\frac{1}{2}$ to 5 minutes) the forequarters will be nearly empty. They contain, on average, a third less milk than the hind quarters and, if the machines are left on unattended at this time, the front teats may be unduly drawn when there is no milk coming down to lubricate the inner linings.

Alternatively, the teat cups may creep up and so constrict the base of the teat that it becomes white, cold and bloodless and quite a hardening can be felt for many minutes after the removal of the cups.

A proper routine will avoid all this. It should be so planned that, towards the end of the free flow of milk, a forward tension is applied to the cluster. At the same time the rear quarters should receive a downward massage between the fingers and thumb so that all four quarters are emptied together.

This last operation should last about one minute; then the teat cups should be removed altogether.

Recent research work in America confirms, from another angle, the importance of proper machine management, es-

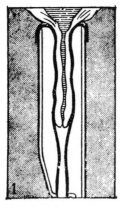 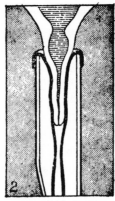

Membranes lining the teat channel at base of udder may be rubbed together when teat cups "creep" up.

When teat cups "draw" the teats, the membranes towards ends of teats are rubbed.

pecially towards the end of the milk flow. It shows that when milking machines are left on cows after the milk flow rate has fallen below 1 lb (454 g) per minute, tissue cells appear in the milk and its chloride content also rises.

These are obvious signs of irritation of the teat linings. They must be avoided if mastitis is to be kept at bay.

DON'T KEEP COWS WAITING

Now all this means that you must have a margin of time in your milking technique. Once the machines are on a cow, she must not be kept waiting for you. You must so organise your routine that you can wait for the cow.

A very useful aid to correct machine milking is the milk-flow indicator which can be fitted to releaser plants. This automatically shows when the stripping point is reached.

The use of the automatic cup-cluster removal system can eliminate any anxiety as to when to remove the cups. No harm is done by leaving a few millilitres of milk in a healthy udder. But you can do serious harm by vigorous stripping.

If you milk by hand, the same principles apply. Get all the milk you can as rapidly as possible by the full hand. Then stop. Rather leave milk behind than drag it out. You will get it when you milk the cow next time and no harm will be done. This will not cause her to dry up.

USE OF DISINFECTANTS

Now there is another aspect of milking routine that we must consider in preventing mastitis. It concerns the use of disinfectants.

These must not only be bactericidal but must be bland to the skin and prevent the formation of sores. A number of such disinfectants including the iodophor type, are now available.

The hypochlorite types of disinfectant sold as approved by the Ministry of Agriculture for these purposes are valuable and do what is intended of them. But they cannot be expected to be effective on surfaces that are thickly covered with dirt or grease.

Moreover, they quickly become inactive when the water in which they are used gets contaminated with milk, hair and dung. What happens is that the chlorine (which is the disinfecting agent) is reduced by the organic matter and is no longer free to act as a germicide.

So, for washing the cows, it is worth making a rule to have a fresh bucket of the solution and a sterile cloth for every five cows. An alternative is to wash with a hose and dry off with a disposable paper towel.

All cloths and buckets should, of course, be sterilised daily.

The practice of rinsing the teat cup clusters in fresh water and then in a chlorine solution between each cow is a wise one when there is an active mastitis infection in the herd. But where there is no mastitis, rinsing in clean water is probably adequate.

In any case I do advise having an enamel or aluminium cup (a strip-cup without the black disc will do) filled with disinfectant solution of the type and strength used for udder washing and immersing each teat rapidly after the cups are removed.

155

This leaves a layer of disinfectant on the skin of teats between milkings and, what is more important, a drop at the tip of each teat to protect the orifice. Using a dual spray for udder cleaning and final disinfection is proving easy, cheap and effective.

There are now a number of good detergents – the quaternary derivatives known as iodophors – on the market which, whilst being equally effective as disinfectants, do not have the same drying and chapping effect, as can occur with the hypochlorites, if the chlorine concentration is raised above the standard of 5 per cent.

A system is now available whereby hot disinfectant can be circulated through the teat cups without passing through the main pipe system. This has been shown to be much more effective than merely dipping the teat cups vigorously in a bucket of disinfectant after each cow has been milked.

There are four other practical hints that I can give you for keeping mastitis away.

The first is: use the type of teat-cup liner that suits your cows. Large Shorthorns, for example, may require a somewhat different liner from Ayrshires. This is a matter which you should discuss with the agent or representative of the manufacturers of your machine.

It is known that the resilience and form of teat-cup liners play an important part in the initiation and prevention of mastitis. Indeed, where there are no obvious causes of an outbreak a change of liners may be a good thing. The old-type rubber liners were apt to retain bacteria in crevices, and because of loss of elasticity as they got older, tended not to expel the milk fully when they contracted. However, modern ones do not have these defects.

The second point is this: have some penicillin cream handy in the cowhouse and make a regular practice of applying it to any teat sores or cracks, but before doing so dry off the teat with a sterilised cloth.

The third is: as far as possible avoid using teat syphons or probing the teats in any way. If an instrument has to be used in an emergency, see that it is properly sterilised beforehand by being kept in boiling water for at least ten minutes. And, in the case of teat obstructions, call in veterinary aid; there may be mastitis organisms present and special treatment may be necessary in conjunction with the operation.

The fourth is: during the summer months make a habit of using a modern fly repellent spray on the cows and in the cowshed itself so that the fly menace is practically eliminated during milking.

WHEN MASTITIS OCCURS

Mastitis may occur in several different forms, as under:

MILD – A few clots are seen in the foremilk only. They may appear at each milking or sometimes intermittently. There are no obvious adverse effects on the cow, but milk yield will be lower than normal. This variety is often passed off as a "chill." It is dangerous because it may flare up at any time.

ACUTE – The quarter is hot, swollen and painful, the skin being deep pink or red. Milk is usually straw-coloured and sometimes stained with blood. (In "summer" mastitis it may look like pus and have a foul smell). Cow is usually upset, off her feed, not cudding, may grind her teeth and have high temperature.

While you are waiting for veterinary attention, it is a wise practice to strip out the affected quarter at about two-hourly intervals. And that should be done, of course, into a vessel containing disinfectant so that the germs are immediately destroyed.

It would also be helpful to apply hot fomentations wherever there is heat, pain or swelling.

But, once your vet has examined the cow, he will give you more detailed advice according to the circumstances in each case and, later, according to the laboratory report and the treatment he has to give.

SUB-ACUTE – Runs a similar course to above but of shorter duration. There may be only slight rise in temperature and appetite may not be entirely lost. Quarter is less congested and painful.

CHRONIC – The last two types may ultimately resolve themselves into this form. The quarter is painless but more or less thickened and feels appreciably firmer than a normal quarter. Secretion is ropey or like clotted cream, without smell. Animal's general health is unaffected.

HOW TO DEAL WITH MASTITIS

Apart from the *Streptococcus agalactiae*, mastitis may be due to other streptoccocci, to staphylococci, to *C. pyogenes*, to tuberculosis. On occasions it may be caused by the actinomycosis fungus, by yeasts or even by *E. coli* (often associated with over-milking). Pseudomonas organisms are now increasingly being identified in the milk. When this occurs external factors such as a dirty water supply are to be suspected. Sometimes mixed infections are encountered. Indeed, cases do arise in which no infections can be found – so-called physiological types.

Modern remedies are very much better than they were even five years ago and the types of synthetic penicillin available are effective over a wider range of bacteria. Treatment, however, has been made more complicated by new regulations protecting humans from the allergic rashes which occasionally occur due to drinking milk containing antibiotics or their residues.

A high level of antibiotic is necessary to destroy the organisms, but the milk cannot be used until the penicillin is almost undetectable. Therefore the penicillin used must be quickly effective and disappear rapidly – the so-called high-level, short-acting method. Within 48 hours after the original intra-mammary infusion very little is left. On the reasonable assumption that most cases are due to the common pathogens this treatment should be applied at the first hint of trouble.

Some forms of mastitis do not respond well to any form of treatment, but (except in the case of a tuberculosis infection) your vet will give injections to arrest the progress of the disease and keep its ill effects as small as possible, and advise on routine.

In the case of mastitis arising from a tuberculosis infection, it will, of course, be necessary to have the cow slaughtered under the Tuberculosis Order. She would constitute what is technically known as an "open" case of tb. and would be shedding dangerous tubercle bacilli.

HERD PROBLEMS

The foregoing remarks have referred to the treatment of individual cases of the disease, but on so many farms outbreaks occur involving up to 50 per cent or more of the herd.

In such cases immediate steps should be taken to have a laboratory examination made of a bulk milk sample of each cow. By this method the type and distribution of the causal bacteria will be established.

"BLITZ" TREATMENT

In an extensive outbreak all quarters of all cows may be treated, or it may be considered only necessary to treat all quarters of infected cows according to the number of animals affected. A further set of samples is taken in a few weeks' time and those animals which are still carrying the mastitis organisms are once more treated.

Assuming that suitable hygienic measures are also introduced this will result in a marked reduction in the number of affected animals. There will, however, be a small proportion still affected by other types of bacteria or having quarters that have become so thickened and fibrous that no treatment can be expected to bring about a complete cure.

Those which still have infections – even if not of the streptococcal variety – should be given a second treatment, possibly combined with some other drug.

After this there will be a small residual number of incurable cases which should be isolated, milked last and – unless your vet considers it worth while treating them – disposed of at the earliest possible moment.

Continuous culling is, however, very wasteful and not to be encouraged. There are now very effective methods which can be employed on a herd basis, apart from treating the individual animal, which reduce the overall incidence to a very low level.

THE DRY COW

Many animals are dried off with mastitis organisms still in the udder; some may become infected by contact during the dry period. This is the period when maximum benefit can be achieved by treatment, the situation being greatly helped by the use of long-acting penicillins such as Orbenin. Treatment should be applied after the last milking before drying off. This procedure has proved very effective in reducing the incidence of existing infections and preventing fresh ones arising.

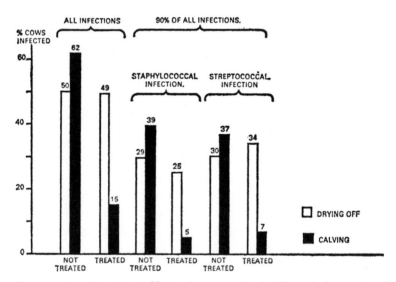

Histogram shows the success in 35 typical commercial herds (888 cows) of a proprietary bactericidal preparation plus teat dipping in controlling infection present in drying off and the incidence of new infection during the dry period.

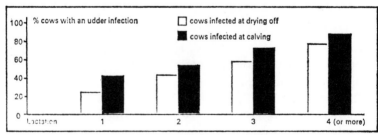

In the untreated herd, infection increases with each successive lactation.

(With acknowledgements to Beechams Research Laboratories)

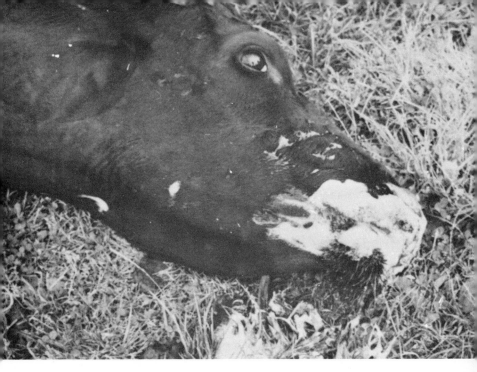

Hypomagnesaemia is caused by a deficiency of magnesium in the bloodstream. The affected animal shivers, staggers around and finally falls down in a fit, frothing at the mouth.

HYPOMAGNESAEMIA

Prevention is by feeding magnesium in the cows' normal feed, or special magnesium-enriched feeds may be purchased. Where hypomagnesaemia is a major problem, it can be counteracted by treating soil and pasture with magnesium limestone or calcined magnesite.

Cows become unsettled during milking if bothered by flies, and this can have a detrimental effect on milk yields. One way to keep flies out of the parlour is by siting in the entrance doorway a water spray under which the cows must pass.

Alternatively, spraying with an electrical mist gun will rid the building of flies and many other troublesome pests. It can also double for use in the grain store or poultry house.

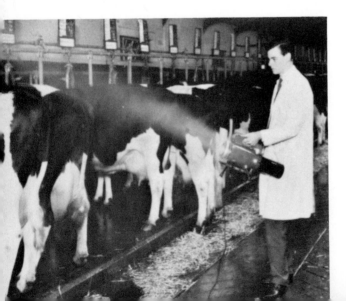

nd outside

An automatic insecticide spray through which the cows must pass when coming in from grazing. Treatment such as this several times a year will go a long way towards keeping the cattle free from pests.

Dungsteads provide a welcome breeding ground for all types of pests. To prevent this, a residual spray can be used on the heap.

This three-month-old calf is showing signs of
copper deficiency. Its hair is rough and dull,
there is a loss of pigmentation with the appearance of a greyish-white zone around the eyes,
and the animal is somewhat dejected.

HAVE THOROUGH CLEAN-UP

After a herd treatment of this kind do not forget that the maintenance of a clean herd is now very largely in your care. Dirty hands, dirty stalls, faulty use of a milking machine, etc. all encourage the persistence of this disease. And it must be remembered that some of the streptococci (*S. uberis, S. dysgalactiae*) can live and multiply away from the cow and are to be found on anything the milker handles such as electric-light switches, broom handles, bucket handles, etc. Since the introduction of cubicles there has been mounting evidence to suggest that the sawdust bedding may provide a good breeding ground for mastitis organisms, especially *S. uberis* and *S. dysgalactia.*

All these points should therefore receive attention when a "blitz" is being carried out.

It is true that some people consider the elimination of the common streptococcal type of mastitis as paving the way to an increase of other types. There is no real evidence that substitution has, in fact, taken place.

THE CELL COUNT

Having adopted the above methods of treatment and control, one can improve the situation still further by anticipating cases. Chronic and sub-chronic cases can go un-noticed, either because the milker does not use the strip cup and take notice of the first milk in which there may be small flakes or pus, or because changes in the milk are still not marked enough to be visible.

Normal milk contains cells shed from the wall linings or actually from the secreting tissues. The numbers are relatively small, but if inflammation arises from any cause these tend to increase and many leucocytes, which have invaded the tissues, are shed as well. When the latter become excessive, as they do when inflammation becomes severe, there is cause for concern and as a result of recent research into the nature and number of cells occurring under different circumstances, it is now possible to interpret the results, defining them roughly into *normal, suspicious* and *serious* cases. In the latter group cases will quickly be obvious on inspection, but it is when there are cases occurring in the middle 'suspicious' group that further investigation is indicated, individual cows being identified and treated.

Occasional cell counts may be made when insipient cases will be revealed, but regular monthly counts of bulked herd milk is well worth while, enabling early action to be taken and preventing milk of undesirable quality (having an unpleasant taste) from reaching the consumer.

The following figures provide a general guide and are of interest. If herd bulk sample cell counts are consistently over 1,000,000 cells per ml, then it is likely that the mastitis situation in the herd is severe and from 60-80 per cent of cows will be affected. If between 750,000 and 1,000,000 cells per ml, 40-60 per cent may be affected, whilst if the cell count is between 50,000 and 500,000 cells per ml, 20-40 per cent of the cows have mastitis and below 50,000 cells per ml the number of affected cows is probably less than 20 per cent.

Mycoplasma Mastitis

Organisms of this class are widely associated with respiratory conditions in man and animals and can cause arthritis. The picture of infection is characteristic. Young animals are mostly affected. One or more quarters may be markedly swollen, giving milk with a fine, white, powdery deposit and no smell. There is little if any general effect. The cell count rises in 24 hours and clinical signs appear in three days.

If the infection occurs within six weeks of calving, animals usually recover spontaneously. If later, then it persists and carries over to the next lactation.

Calves suffering from respiratory trouble are commonly the origin of an outbreak, transmitting the organism whilst suckling. Teat-liners may be affected.

Summer Mastitis

At this stage I think it worth while elaborating the advice I gave in the chapter about care of the cow before calving with reference to summer mastitis – usually caused by the germ *C. pyogenes.*

Dairy farmers whose herds are subject to this infection have a special problem. But, again, it is one most likely to be solved by taking precautions against its attack for, so far, we have no satisfactory cure for it.

We still do not know how the germ gains access to the udder. It is often present in other parts of the cow's body and may make its way down to the udder from inside. It may be carried to the udder by infected flies alighting on the teats and particularly on the teat openings where drops of milk may hang.

If the germs are already in the body, there is not much you can do about matters. But you can take steps to prevent flies from infecting your down-calvers.

WORTH-WHILE MEASURES

Tackle the manure heaps – the flies' breeding grounds – by spraying with DDT or gammexane and by packing the sides with soil or, preferably, by storing the manure in brick or concrete-walled pits so that there is no seepage.

Make sure that your in-calvers are not given a low-lying and closely-wooded pasture. An upland grazing would be better.

Here again the appropriate long-acting penicillin should be infused into the udder of the animal prior to turning out dry.

When they are turned out take special precautions to see that their teats are adequately sealed. Wipe the teats thoroughly with methylated spirits first then dip each teat into an egg cup about threequarters full with collodion. This dries quickly, and a thick layer of Stockholm tar can then be painted on as an additional precaution.

Such a seal (which should also be applied to the teats of down-calving heifers) should be effective for the entire dry period, but it would be a wise precaution to examine the teats carefully at frequent intervals and to renew any seal that seems to need attention.

WATCH DOWN-CALVERS

Lastly, you should make a point of looking over the down-calvers regularly. Watch for any signs of distress in an animal

163

– standing apart from the herd, paddling with the hind feet and staring ahead instead of grazing – and straightway examine the udder for any abnormality. It may show itself first as a hardness in one quarter but not necessarily then accompanied by a swelling or inflammation, although this will follow at a later stage.

The condition is serious. The animal's life is in danger and immediate treatment is essential to prevent the poisons that are produced from killing the cow.

If matters are taken soon enough and antibiotic injections are given sufficiently early, they may do some good as it is now known that an organism called a micrococcus (which is susceptible) infects the udder first and appears to pave the way for the *C. pyogenes* invasion.

Stripping and massage every hour will help matters while you are waiting for veterinary attention. Strip into a utensil containing disinfectant and ensure that this is emptied down a drain immediately after use so that there is no opportunity for flies to alight on the strippings and so spread the disease.

As far as treatment is concerned there is no certain cure, though modern remedies are very much more effective than those used even five years ago, since the 'spectrum' of bacterial coverage (kill) has greatly increased. Prompt action may however save a quarter, and dry cow therapy is well worth while.

In this type of mastitis – as with others – injury may well play a very significant rôle. When calves are kept in bunches in restricted spaces they become bored and frequently suckle each other. Their sharp teeth may well damage the delicate immature udder tissue of their companions and so pave the way for the establishment of mastitis germs.

Well, it's not difficult to boil down this advice about mastitis to something practical. In fact, it's a practical job, and mainly your job.

Even for the varieties of mastitis for which we have no certain cure there is a considerable chance of prevention through proper cowshed hygiene. But, for streptococcal mastitis there is not only a complete answer in your vet's penicillin, there is a complete answer on the farm in the routine you can adopt.

CHAPTER XI

BOVINE TUBERCULOSIS

ALTHOUGH it can be taken for certain that the cattle of this country are largely free of bovine tuberculosis, and milk supplies are accordingly safe, a small residual infection is likely to remain for some years. Experience in many countries has shown that it is easier to reduce the incidence of infection from 20 per cent down to 2 per cent than from 2 per cent to anything less. This is probably due, in part at least, to the existence of non-specific infections and to reservoirs of infection which cause reinfection of cattle. But, true it is that as time goes on, a smaller percentage of those animals slaughtered show visible lesions.

It will be remembered that the test used is a double intra-dermal one, which will pick out animals sensitised to the avian tubercle bacillus. Such animals are rarely affected clinically and subsequently may lose their sensitivity. They are not eliminated from the herd. A bovine reaction, however, may be due to skin tuberculosis or to an infection of human origin. In fact, the situation has now been reached when the human is more dangerous to the cow than the cow to the human!

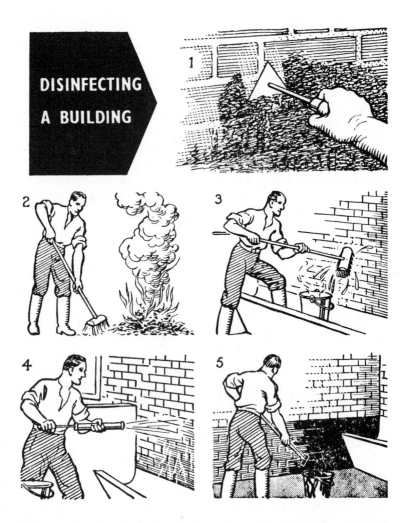

DISINFECTING A BUILDING

1. *Scrape all surfaces thoroughly.*   2. *Burn all scrapings and sweepings.*   3. *Scrub with hot soda water.* (*Water near boiling; handful soda per 2 gallons (9 litres)*).
4. *Spray with disinfectants.*   5. *Creosote or whitewash as required.*
Other methods of disinfection include steam sterilisation and fumigation where the building permits.

166

RESERVOIRS OF INFECTION

Progressive tuberculosis due to the bovine strain of organism may be encountered in goats and swine, and although originally contracted from cattle, may continue in such communities so tending to re-infect the former livestock. Goats have a strong natural resistance and are not often infected with either the bovine or human type, but pigs are fully susceptible to bovine tb, and the incidence, prior to eradication in the bovine species, was appreciable. Cases are, however, becoming less and less frequent.

The human strain of the organism has a very low degree of infectivity for cattle and cases occur but rarely. However, infection of this type now assumes a relatively enhanced importance, being responsible for a positive tuberculin test. Isolated pockets of infection with the bovine type also exist in wild life especially, alas, in the badger population in certain limited areas of the south-west of England. Owing to the existence of such reservoirs of infection it will be necessary to continue to test all cattle at least every three years for some time to come.

CHAPTER XII

DEALING WITH RESPIRATORY DISEASES

IT'S a good idea to make yourself familiar with the sound of air passing into a cow's lungs. Try it out on one or two of your animals. Put your ear against the chest, just behind the elbow, and listen.

You will hear a soft sighing sound as the air is drawn in, then, after a momentary pause, the same sound again as the air is breathed out.

That is a very different sound from what you will hear when there is an inflammation or an infection of the respiratory tract.

In the early stages of trouble the normal sighing sounds increase; as the disease progresses they become more like a rushing blast; but then, as the lungs become more solid with blood, catarrhal fluid and mucus, there may be no sound of air movement at all.

CRISIS STAGE

That is the crisis stage.

The animal may die from suffocation or absorption of poisonous products from the lungs, or it may turn the crisis and start to get better. In this case the consolidation of the lungs slowly breaks down and you can hear a rattling in the air tubes as the animal breathes more and more freely.

Obviously it is our job to try and prevent the crisis stage ever being reached. How can we do it?

First of all, let us study what happens when a cow breathes.

The air passes through the nose, over the back of the throat, through the larynx, down the windpipe and then through the bronchii to the deeper parts of the lungs.

Any part of this respiratory tract may become inflamed. If it happens to the larynx, the animal has laryngitis; if it happens to the bronchii, she has bronchitis; if the pleura – the membrane that lines the ribs and covers the lungs – she has pleurisy; if the lungs themselves are affected, she has pneumonia.

There can be many reasons for inflammation occurring. I will deal with them all, but I want to put the most frequent cause first.

Chills

If we could prevent chills, we should stop many cases of respiratory troubles in cows. But we can't prevent them; they are mainly caused through sudden and extreme changes of temperature and weather that are beyond our control.

Nevertheless, they may have a vital effect. They can so upset the normal conditions in the respiratory tract that the bacteria there, instead of remaining harmless, become active and get the upper hand. The blood capillaries are dilated giving a reddish appearance and the mucus glands become very active. In fact, inflammation has set in. The surface cells are shed off and, together with bacteria, are caught up in the mucus. The catarrhal discharge from the nose and mouth is an indication that this is happening.

What we have to do is to make sure that this is dealt with before it goes too far.

So it is necessary to be on the look-out for chills, particularly in the autumn and during mild winter weather when sudden changes are likely. And the signs to look for in an affected animal are:

1. Shivering.
2. First heavy breathing and then rapid and shallow breathing, with practically no rise and fall of the chest walls.
3. The nose slightly lifted and thrust forward.
4. Temperature up, may be as high as 41°C.
5. Milk yield down.
6. Slight dampness of coat as in perspiration.
7. A dry nose.

The essentials for quick recovery are warmth and fresh air.

Therefore, as quickly as possible, get the animal into a loose box that is well ventilated. But avoid draughts.

Then rug the cow.

If you have proper blankets for the job, well and good. If not, use sacks – thick ones.

Don't open them out; stitch two together lengthways, lay them on the cow so that the join runs down the backbone and secure the two front corners by a cord across the brisket and the two back corners by a cord behind the rump. A loosely tied cord running right round the girth over the sacking will also help to prevent it from slipping off.

If the animal is in a really bad way, don't be content with that. Get an assistant to help you pack a three-inch or four-inch

RUGGING
A COW

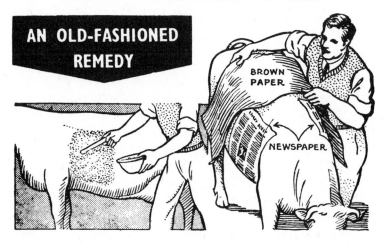

AN OLD-FASHIONED REMEDY

BROWN PAPER

NEWSPAPER

(76-100 mm) layer of straw on top of the sacking and secure it in position by putting another pair of sacks on the top of that.

And do give liberal bedding. Use three or four times what you would put into a box for a healthy cow. Select straw that is not dusty and shake it up well so that the animal is knee-deep in it. It will encourage body warmth.

MUSTARD PLASTER

Now a lot of people, including many veterinary surgeons, believe in the old-fashioned mustard plaster for this trouble. I agree with them; it is well worth applying.

To prepare it you simply mix up a quarter of a pound of mustard with cold water to make a stiff paste. Then, using a piece of smooth flat wood – or the back of the mixing spoon – smear it on to both sides of the cow's chest. The sketch will show just where. Antiphlogistine can be used in the same way.

Apply as evenly as possible. Then cover each side with a piece of newspaper and follow that by placing a single sheet of brown paper right over the cow's back so that it drapes over both sides. When that is in position, replace the sacking.

In 24 hours the mustard or antiphlogistine will have done its job. The papers can be removed and the material brushed out

171

of the coat if you wish. I should not advise repeating a mustard plaster; it might easily blister thin-skinned animals.

GIVE GRUELS

As regards food, there are two "don'ts" to mention:

Don't drench the cow. In respiratory troubles there is often difficulty in swallowing. A drench may easily "go the wrong way" and make matters very much worse.

When the animal is able to take liquids herself, she can have a sustaining cornflour or oatmeal gruel made with milk.

Don't give any long fodder. Tempt the cow with a few tasty bits and pieces – a handful of crushed oats or some calf-nuts – to try and get her to eat.

But don't leave the same lot in front of her for too long. Take it away, even if it hasn't been touched, and replace it with a fresh supply.

Once the animal starts eating you can keep her needs supplied with small quantities at frequent intervals. Introduce a few wisps of really soft, green (but not dusty) hay; a little leafy kale would also probably be welcome.

USEFUL MEDICINE

As the gruel drinks are eased off you can put 4 ounces (113 g) of Epsom salts and one-quarter ounce (7 g) of potassium nitrate in a gallon (4·5 l) of drinking water each day for three days.

If the patient becomes "chesty", then it is a good plan to give one of the proprietary cough pastes that can be obtained from veterinary chemists. Give it according to directions; the best method is usually to apply the appropriate amount on the tongue with a piece of smooth flat wood.

The rugging should remain in position until the cow is fully recovered. Even then it's best to be guided by the weather. Choose a mild spell and remove the sacks in the morning rather than at evening time when the air may be getting chilly again.

An added precaution is to do the job in two stages. Replace the thick sacks with an opened-out light sack first, and discard the light sack a day or two later.

That is the basic farm treatment for all respiratory troubles. It should, in nine cases out of ten, put right a chill and prevent it from developing into a serious matter. But it may not work in the tenth case; pleurisy (inflammation of the membrane lining the chest cavity) or pneumonia (where the lung tissue itself is involved) may develop. And, while it would alleviate respiratory trouble due to bacteria, viruses or mycoplasmas, it would not cure the condition.

Therefore it is wise to seek veterinary advice in all cases that do not respond speedily to farm attention. Your vet will be able to make an accurate differential diagnosis and so determine the correct treatment.

Fog Fever

There are several forms of respiratory distress, mostly associated with adult stock, which cause considerable economic loss. Although there is no ideal remedy, an understanding of the conditions of management under which the particular outbreak has occurred, will, with post mortem evidence, help to identify one condition from another and so enable appropriate measures to be taken. Recent work has successfully identified fog fever from other similar conditions.

Fog fever is an out-of-doors disease occurring in the autumn (September, November, October in the UK) when cattle are turned out onto what is loosely described as 'foggage' or 'aftermath'. Only mature beef-type single suckling animals, generally over two years old and in good condition, seem to be involved – not dairy animals.

Symptoms develop in 90 per cent of cases within two weeks of the move from poor to significantly better pasture (good grass or, rarely, brassicae). The cattle are usually in a hungry state, and in most cases the pasture on to which they are turned has received fertiliser treatment. Symptoms occur more rapidly under these circumstances than when no treatment has been applied.

Thirty per cent of animals may die in some outbreaks and none in others, though in the latter up to 60 per cent of the herd may be involved and in the acute cases death occurs within two days of the onset of symptoms. It would seem that exposure to stress factors, such as the excitement associated with movement from one pasture to another, is a precipitating factor. Previous exposure to husk-infested pastures, is unassociated with this condition. Though the cause is not yet clear, it is obviously associated with the nature of the pastures and the state and treatment of the animal when moved.

Clinically, the animals are in good condition, very alert and *not coughing* but showing marked respiratory distress with a loud expiratory grunt, frothing at the mouth and mouthbreathing. The rate of breathing is greatly increased, but a rise in temperature is rare. A paper-like crackling under the skin due to air is sometimes encountered.

When an outbreak occurs, stock should be moved to poorer pastures or indoors, with an absolute minimum of stress. To prevent the trouble, grazing should be organised so as to avoid the sudden introduction of hungry adult cattle to better pastures. Start by using pre-grazed aftermath or strip-grazing.

Adult Husk

Husk, already referred to, is generally regarded as a disease of the young animal. But in animals over two years of age, including milking cows, outbreaks of severe coughing are not infrequently associated with active parasitic bronchitis or due to an allergic reaction created by re-exposure to an affected pasture (generally, again, an aftermath in the autumn), they themselves having had an attack of husk when younger. No adult parasites may be present, but larvae may be found in the lung fringes.

Other Respiratory Conditions

It now seems certain that a number of these very severe and dramatic cases are associated with the presence of moulds such as *aspergillus fumigatus* and *thermopolyspora polyspora* (the cause of 'farmer's lung'). These can be identified in the lung tissue in affected animals. In view of the ubiquitous nature of these

OUT-OF-DOOR TREATMENT

Little if anything can be done when an outbreak has occurred. On balance it is probably better to allow affected animals to remain outside in the fresh air and to offer them good quality hay. Pneumonia may, however, quickly supervene so a careful watch must be kept on all animals in the affected batch.

Some success in the control of fog fever appears to have been achieved by dosing monthly for worms. This will clear out bowel parasites, and, by avoiding a loss of condition, enable the animal to recover more readily or even prevent it from becoming seriously affected.

Much work is still being carried out on this disease.

Anaphylaxis

As with asthma in human beings we have already noted above that fog fever can be a state of anaphylaxis due to the effect of certain moulds. A large variety of agents can also cause sensitivity leading to an allergic reaction which may take the form of a skin rash, blisters or "blain", sometimes with marked respiratory distress. Cases have been recorded in association with wheat, maize, soya bean, rice bran, clovers and certain pasture plants. There is oedema of the eyelids, face and vulva with or without oedematous plaques over the trunk and brisket.

Treatment will depend upon the symptoms.

Pasteurellosis

There are also cases of pneumonia caused by a germ known as *Pasteurella boviseptica*. This condition resembles 'flu in its acuteness and severity.

There is a rise in temperature, a loss of appetite and a marked depression in affected animals. There may be discharges from the nose and eyes; there may be diarrhoea and dysentery, coughing and possibly swelling in the throat and neck causing difficulty in breathing.

This disease can take one of three forms: the peracute – with sudden fever, haemorrhages on the mucous membranes followed by collapse and death within 24 hours; the acute –

persistent diarrhoea and wasting, also accompanied by pneumonia.

CONTROL MEASURES

Because of the need to differentiate the disease from anthrax, cattle plague or pleuro-pneumonia (which are all notifiable) and black-quarter and bracken poisoning, veterinary diagnosis is recommended as early as possible.

The disease usually passes rapidly from one animal to another. So it is essential to introduce control measures immediately.

Affected stock should be isolated; they should be kept warm and generally treated as described for cases of chill. But they will certainly need veterinary attention and the specific remedies that only a vet can give if fatalities are to be avoided.

Pasteurellosis may develop as a secondary condition after husk has become established and paved the way for further infections. This is more likely in adult cattle than in heifers or calves. An animal may apparently recover from husk but the violent cough sometimes causes permanent lung damage with bleeding and exudation at a later date.

Virus Pneumonia

Intensive animal husbandry has been largely responsible for the increased incidence of what is known as virus pneumonia. The situation is complicated by the fact that at least three viruses are involved, namely: (1) Para influenza, (2) Bovine Adeno Virus, (3) Bedsonia. These invade the respiratory system, so damaging the tissues that resident bacteria can enter and set up inflammation.

Animals of 8-16 weeks of age are by far the most susceptible. The symptoms will vary according to the combination of pathogens present, the challenge dose and the environment in which the animals are kept. The disease flourishes where indoor stocking rates are high, batch segregation is poor, contact between groups is easy, humidity is high, ventilation bad and feeding irregular.

SOME
POISONOUS PLANTS

Above: Laurel; *left:* black bryony; *below left:* garden nightshade; *below right:* ragwort.

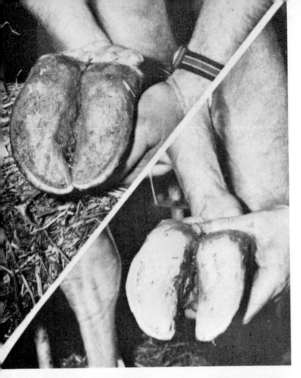

FOOT
CARE
. . . PARING

If a cow's feet are not trimmed regularly, the toes become overgrown and the soles rounded and susceptible to bruising. Here we see an example of (top) a foot requiring attention and (bottom) after paring.

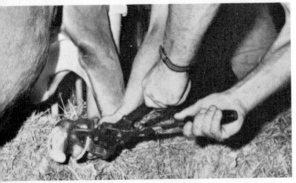

To pare a cow's feet, first clean each foot thoroughly with a stiff brush and clip off as much of the overgrown horn as possible without cutting into the quick.

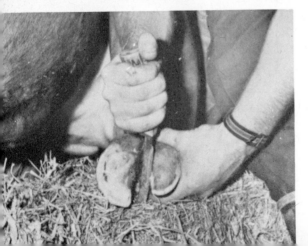

Finally, trim the horn inside the cleft with a sharp knife, finishing off by shaping the hoof and rounding off rough edges with a rasp.

... REMOVING
A STONE

A cow can often pick up a small stone in the foot, which penetrates the sole and causes discomfort and, if not treated, lameness. When a cow shows signs of discomfort, tap the hoof—the cow will react violently when the affected part is tapped.

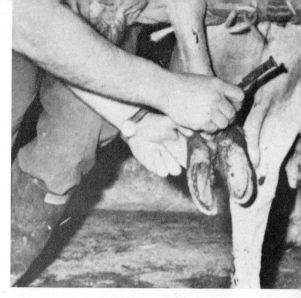

Next, clean off the hoof with a brush and rasp it to remove superficial cracks and blemishes. Cut the affected area away until the foreign body can be located and removed.

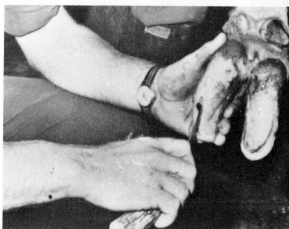

Finally, treat the wound with an antiseptic or antibiotic in aerosol or powder form. Keep the cow on clean concrete until the foot is healing well and she is able to walk without discomfort.

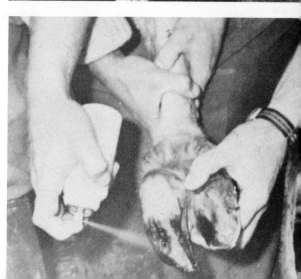

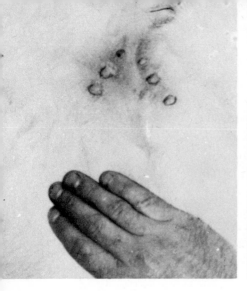

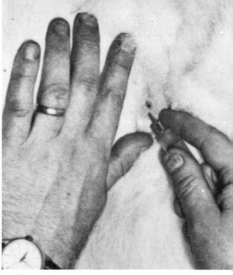

This heifer has six teats. The normal ones are the larger, which are correctly spaced. It is the two small teats which are the unwanted extras and will have to be removed.

After clipping the hair short and washing the area with antiseptic, inject $\frac{1}{2}$ cc of local anaesthetic under the skin at the base of each extra teat and wait for at least a minute for it to take effect.

REMOVING SUPERNUMERARY TEATS

With a strong pair of tweezers, pull each unwanted teat outwards as far as possible and cut it off with a curved pair of scissors. To remove the rudimentary milk sinus and avoid leaving behind an unsightly bump, cut well into each teat base.

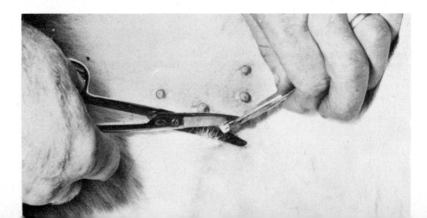

To take these points separately. Disease spreads by droplet infection following coughing and sneezing. So the closer contact – the greater amount of animals together, the greater the risk of spread. High humidity encourages the transport of viruses and cold, fluctuating temperatures are debilitating to the calves.

Recommendations – House should be airy, well ventilated at all times with an ambient temperature of from 13 to 15·6° C. Groups of 5-6 calves are ideal in pens with solid partitions high enough to prevent contact. Fresh batches of calves should be put into properly disinfected pens and never next to one holding already infected animals. A holding unit for imported calves is ideal, keeping them separate for a fortnight to allow any insipient infection to develop. An all-in, all-out policy for the main calf house is recommended.

Fortunately there is now a vaccine available known as Plurovax. The first does can be given as soon as the calf is two weeks old. The second one month later, no further booster dose being necessary.

Infectious Bovine Rhinotracheitis (I.B.R.)

This disease, caused by a virus, first made its appearance in the UK in 1962 but is now quite common. It affects mainly young animals. The incubation period is three days and recovery takes place in about six weeks, some animals subsequently becoming carriers; these can convey the disease to other, healthy stock.

Severe respiratory symptoms are characteristic. Breathing becomes rapid and the breath smells foul due to the presence of necrotic material in the windpipe. Temperature may reach 39·5-42·3 °C. Coughing, conjunctivitis and a nasal and occular discharge are usual with copious salivation – on occasion. Pustular vaginitis with mastitis, abortion and liquifaction of foetus may also be encountered.

Early diagnosis is valuable, and one of the better ways of controlling the disease is to take the temperature of all the animals at risk and to treat all those with a temperature of over 39·5°C with antibiotics. This early intervention reduces the risks of pneumonia from secondary invaders. After three days those with a normal temperature are removed, this process being repeated in a further three days. Total recovery may be complete in a fortnight.

Mucosal Disease

This condition affects animals of all ages and has only recently been recognised as a separate entity, for it bears considerable resemblance to coccidiosis, malignant catarrh, cattle plague and certain forms of corrosive poisoning including that due to acorns.

It is an infectious disease, but its infectivity varies from herd to herd, sometimes only a few animals being affected, at other times an appreciable number.

The mild form is characterised by a brief high temperature, some nasal discharge and diarrhoea of short duration.

The more chronic form mainly attacks adult animals causing considerable suffering but few deaths. Whilst individuals may be affected for two to three weeks, the disease may take several months to run through the herd. There is prolonged, intermittent diarrhoea and loss of milk, and on post-mortem the following changes may be observed: necrosis of the epithelium of the whole alimentary tract from the nasal cavity, pharynx and larynx downwards. In the abomasum and lower intestine catarrhal inflammation, haemorrhage and sometimes ulceration may be noted.

The acute form occurs mainly in young animals from 2-18 months of age and may be associated with 100 per cent mortality. Initially there is loss of appetite and depression, nasal discharge and diarrhoea, a high temperature and marked evidence of thirst.

The diarrhoea may increase in violence until blood-stained mucus appears. This is associated with emaciation, coughing, discharge from the eyes, lameness and ulceration between the claws. Ulceration of the mouth cavity and nose may also be extensive.

Unfortunately there is as yet no known treatment, antibiotics and other remedies being of little value. Recovery, therefore, depends upon good nursing, keeping animals warm and tempting them from time to time with bran mashes and fresh, succulent foods. Stimulant injections might assist recovery.

CHAPTER XIII

TREATMENT OF DIGESTIVE TROUBLES

THE cow's digestive system is a complicated one. It's about 170 feet (51·8 m) long and is big enough to hold anything up to 60 gallons (272·8 l) in the larger cows. That means there is plenty of opportunity for things to go wrong.

But first let us see what happens when things go right. The drawing on page 181 will help us to understand matters clearly.

The food eaten by a cow is coarsely ground by the teeth, is swallowed and goes into the rumen. There it is mixed with saliva and attacked by protozoa and then bacteria which break down the cellulose to digestible products. Vast quantities of bacteria are also produced and used by the cow. There is a continual mechanical "churning" of the rumen to aid the process.

The next stage is the regurgitation of this material into the mouth where it is again chewed to an even finer condition and is well mixed with saliva (chewing the cud).

Then, on being swallowed a second time, the finer particles bypass the rumen and travel via the honeycomb (second stomach), the manyplies (third stomach) into the abomasum (fourth or true stomach), where digestion with peptic juices first commences.

Subsequently digestion (or food breakdown) continues down at least two-thirds of the digestive tract. Absorption or assimilation also takes place along the bowel, leaving behind the indigestible material which passes from the cow as dung.

Intensive research on the phenomenon of rumination has already produced invaluable results which indicate the extreme complexity of the digestion that takes place in this bacterial incubator.

RESULTS OF BAD FEEDING

If the rumen flora is upset by bad feeding or management, signs of ill health will appear. Foods too finely ground may retard rumination; too much succulent food may pass too quickly through the system. Abnormal conditions such as these may not only affect the animal's health but its yield and even the composition of its milk.

Indications are that diseases such as hypomagnesaemia and acetonaemia – dealt with fully elsewhere in this book – may well be initiated by a badly-balanced ration which encourages the production of undesirable substances in the rumen or prevents the rumen microbes and bacteria from breaking down

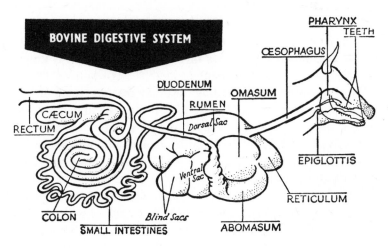

BOVINE DIGESTIVE SYSTEM

PHARYNX
TEETH
OESOPHAGUS
DUODENUM
OMASUM
RUMEN
CÆCUM
RECTUM
Dorsal Sac
EPIGLOTTIS
Ventral Sac
RETICULUM
COLON
Blind Sacs
SMALL INTESTINES
ABOMASUM

181

the food constituents properly and converting them into the essential nutritional needs of the cow.

Indeed it may well be that time and research will show that the general bodily health of the ruminant is intimately related to the fundamental processes of digestion occurring in the rumen.

WHEN THINGS GO RIGHT

The cow gives certain outward signs by which you can judge when her digestive system is working properly.

First, she will usually be seen chewing her cud when she is not actually eating. Secondly, the rumen will be continually in action. If you press your hand in the hollow of the left flank you can feel its movement – an irregular stirring with a sort of "heave" about every 30 seconds. Finally the dung will vary in consistency according to the type of feeding and management.

WHEN THINGS GO WRONG

Now let us trace through the whole process again and deal with the various things that can go wrong.

Loss of appetite associated with a cessation of cudding is usually noticed first, indicating that the rumen has stopped its mechanical churning and regurgitation of food. If so, you will not be able to feel any movement when you press the flank with your hand.

Such a condition may be further complicated by an accumulation of a dense mass of food in the rumen. In this case you will feel a hard and doughy mass through the flank. This is known as an impaction of the rumen.

Now a cow will stop cudding for many reasons; there may be something wrong with the food – it may be unwholesome, musty, mouldy or contain some poisonous matter – or the body may have been exposed to a sudden change in temperature and have become "chilled".

So things start to go wrong. What is to be done?

Obviously, food should be withheld. It is no use packing more into the animal when the system is not dealing with it. That will only make things worse.

Indeed the essential factors for recovery are time and rest.

You may be able to help matters by exercising the animal, by pummelling under the flank if there is an impaction of food and by allowing the animal to have as much water as it cares to drink. You can also give adult cattle 1 pint (57 ml) of linseed oil or 1 lb (454 g) of Epsom salts in a pint (570 ml) of cold water.

Younger cattle should have proportionately smaller doses; heavily pregnant animals should be given one-quarter or one-third size doses which should be repeated three or four times at 4-hourly intervals.

A further precaution would be to rug up an animal that has a temperature.

But I do not advise you to continue farm treatment beyond 12 hours if there is no sign of recovery. Send for help. An operation – rumenotomy – may actually be necessary in the case of an impaction.

So much for the rumen. Now let's go a stage further with the digestive system.

Wire or Nails in Stomach

The second stomach is the spot where foreign bodies that are swallowed with the food usually end up.

Stones and odd nuts and bolts that settle down here don't seem to worry cattle unduly. Many animals are slaughtered and are found to have this kind of museum without having been upset by it.

It's when a piece of wire or a nail is involved that trouble may arise. Here there is a risk of the pointed or twisted end penetrating the wall of the stomach and being forced towards the heart which lies just the other side of the diaphragm. What is known as *traumatic pericarditis* – an inflammation of the covering of the heart – is often the result.

SIGNS OF TROUBLE

Indications of this may take various forms. In the "chronic" type the cow may grunt and show occasional signs of indigestion over a long period and end up by looking continually depressed. She is likely to show wasting.

Where the condition is acute it may be revealed by an arching of the back, paddling with the feet, holding the head uphill, refusing to move. There is a look of pain in the eyes and breathing is shallow and abdominal. A soft short cough is often present.

There is a rough farm test that helps in diagnosing this condition.

Get an assistant to stand at one side of the cow while you remain at the other side. Pass a broom handle under the cow and each of you hold one end of this. Bring the centre of the stick against the cow's belly, about 18 inches (460 mm) in front of the udder and, firmly but quickly, pull the stick upwards.

A normal cow won't mind this, but one that has a piece of wire or nail that has penetrated the stomach will grunt in pain and may even bellow.

An instrument on the principle of the mine detector has been elaborated for use in detecting metallic foreign bodies. This can undoubtedly aid diagnosis but does not differentiate between harmless and dangerous particles.

In a confirmed case the only thing that can be done is an operation to remove the offending material, either via the rumen or by removing a piece of rib to get at the affected part. With

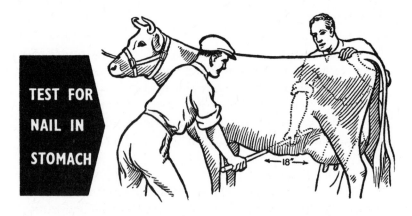

TEST FOR
NAIL IN
STOMACH

—18"—

modern technique there is every reason to expect successful results.

Therefore, should you have reason to suspect that a case of this kind is developing, you should immediately call professional advice.

Scouring

Now we come to the last – or fourth – stomach where true (non-bacterial) digestion of food begins, and the bowel where digestion is continued, but where absorption, or assimilation as it is called, takes place.

The most important guide that everything is all right here is the condition of the dung.

If the dung is loose, the bowel is not (except on spring grass) doing its job properly – food is passing along too quickly. If the dung is hard, bowel action is being retarded.

Scouring is the most common trouble. And the remedy for it depends on finding out the cause.

How does a vet sort things out when he is faced with the problem of scouring?

First of all he wants to know whether the scouring is confined to an individual animal, whether it exists in several individuals or affects a high proportion of the herd.

Suppose a large part of the herd is involved. In that case his first line of enquiry will be the diet. These are the kind of questions he will ask:

(a) Has there been a too-sudden change in diet? Even if a new food is perfectly wholesome, the fauna and flora of the rumen may be upset by a sudden drastic change.

(b) Has there been a change in grazing?

(c) Has musty food been fed?

(d) Have frozen roots or greens been given?

(e) Are the stock over-fed? Is poisoning possible?

(f) Are sugarbeet tops being fed without counteracting the oxalic acid present by well sprinkling them with 2-2½ lb (907 g-1·13 kg) of chalk per ton (tonne) of tops or letting them wilt for at least six hours before feeding?

(g) Have the cattle picked up any poisonous weeds or poisons?

You should not need a veterinary surgeon to find out if one of these is responsible. You ought to be able to track down the cause for yourself. In fact, by exercising proper care in management and feeding, you should have prevented the trouble from occurring.

RISK WITH POISON BAITS

Perhaps a special word is needed on the matter of poisons for rats or mice in view of the increasing use of these, for especial care needs to be taken to ensure that they are not placed where stock, particularly inquisitive young animals, may gain access to them. Two or three feet (0·92-1·2 m) in a drain or drainpipe is a suitable place.

In the control of rats, red squill, arsenic and zinc phosphide are no longer used, but warfarin, which has many advantages, is widely employed. This is fortunately relatively harmless to livestock except in very high doses taken over a number of days. It would probably take 2-3 milligrams of warfarin per kilogram of body weight given for four or five days to have any effect upon calves. Warfarin prevents the blood from clotting so that large haemorrhages may be found at post-mortem.

OTHER CAUSES OF BOWEL TROUBLE

Now let us deal with some specific causes of bowel disturbance. These are:

1. Plant poisoning – ragwort; bracken; acorn; woody nightshade; bryony; dog's mercury; horsetail; hemlock.

2. Mineral poisoning – arsenic; lead; molybdenum (teart); herbicides; insecticides; rat poisons.

3. Parasitic – stomach and bowel worms.

4. Bacterial – black scours; salmonellosis; Johne's disease.

Bracken Poisoning

This is well known in some parts of the country. It is most likely to occur towards the end of a dry season when cattle are attracted by anything green to eke out sparse grass supplies. If the bracken rhizomes are eaten, poisoning may well be acute since this part of the plant is about five times as toxic as the fronds. So don't put cattle on ploughed bracken land. Symptoms may not appear for 3-4 weeks after cattle have been removed from sources of bracken.

There may be constipation in the early stages, but the main symptoms are scouring and straining with blood-stained droppings, a harsh and staring coat and muscular twitchings.

The first step, obviously, is to move the cattle so that they no longer have access to bracken.

Treatment may be successful if the trouble is taken early enough. There is some evidence that injections of vitamin B_1 (thiamin) may be useful. Your vet may try them. You can drench affected stock very carefully with about one pint (570 ml) each of oatmeal gruel, containing four ounces (113 g) of bakers' yeast.

Ragwort Poisoning

This well-known weed does more damage than any other. Whilst acute symptoms of poisoning closely resemble those due to bracken, a great deal of indirect loss occurs due to unthriftiness and reduced milk yield, the explanation of which is not revealed until death – when the characteristic swelling and hardening of the liver (cirrhosis) is to be seen. Every effort should be made to eliminate this weed.

The insidious nature of this disease and the progressive deterioration of the liver, even after animals have been removed from the source of contamination, is likely to result in marked interference with the liver function, which could possibly explain failures to respond to milk fever treatment and recurrent acetonaemia later.

If you spray grassland and crops with herbicides or insecticides or if you employ a contractor to do this for you then you should see that every precaution is taken to prevent cattle from having contact with the spray material.

Full or empty containers should not be left lying around; care should be taken when filling the tank so that none of the spray is spilt; only the required amount of spray should be applied; stock should be kept off the sprayed area for the length of time specified in the instructions; any risk of the spray entering the drinking water supply must be particularly watched.

Groundnut Poisoning

A fungus known as *Aspergillus flavus* has now been identified in association with samples of groundnut from almost every part of the world. Attention was first directed to the dangers of such contamination when a vast number of turkeys died in 1960, in whose rations Brazilian groundnut was included.

All young animals appear to be susceptible in varying degrees to the toxin (known as aflatoxin) produced by the fungus, and calves are no exception.

Acorn Poisoning

Acorns, if taken in large quantities, can cause scouring. But a characteristic feature of this trouble is that the scouring alternates with constipation – a hard black dung – especially in the early stages. There may also be signs of blood in the dung. Further, the symptoms may not appear until several days after the acorns have been eaten.

This upset is caused by the tannic acid principle in acorns.

The best antidote is 1 pint (570 ml) of linseed oil followed two hours later with ½ an ounce (14 g) of ammonium carbonate. One or two ounces (28-56 g) of chlorodyne may be given if the animal is in pain.

Mineral Poisoning

The main trouble to be considered under this heading is a disease known as "teart" – now well understood and under control in the localities involved, *e.g.* Somerset and, to a lesser extent, parts of Warwickshire. It is caused by grazing fields in which the soil has a high molybdenum content. Hay from such pastures will also give trouble, although to a lesser extent.

The presence of the metal (which has no nutritional value) interferes with the proper action of the bowel and the uptake of copper.

The symptoms of this are very much like Johne's disease, except that a large number of animals is usually affected and it occurs from 10 to 21 days after the stock has been turned out, especially in the spring and early summer. There is a drop in milk yield, wasting and violent diarrhoea with a characteristic brownish-grey colour.

Until the disease was mastered, treatment consisted of removing the stock from affected fields and giving them, night and morning, drenches of 10 ounces (283 g) of a one per cent copper sulphate solution until bowels were normal.

Now research has given us a preventive. It involves feeding copper-fortified compound cake mixtures, with the application of copper to the pastures as an additional safeguard.

This is now a matter of course in districts where teart is to be expected.

Sugarbeet and Mangold Poisoning
(*Nitrate and Oxalic Acid Poisoning*)

The leaves of both these plants contain oxalic acid and poisoning may occur if they are not allowed to wilt or treated with chalk (see under Scouring). The roots also contain oxalic acid and nitrates. Mangolds may contain as much as 12 per cent acid (on a dry-matter basis). Twenty pounds (9·07 kg) of roots contain 0·068 per cent of oxalic acid which is equivalent to 95·2 grains, and 160 grains of oxalic acid is toxic for a 1,000-lb (453·6 kg) animal.

It is unwise to feed the roots before Christmas, *i.e.* until the oxalic acid has broken down. Even then it is important not to introduce large quantities suddenly. The rumen bacteria can deal with increasing quantities of oxalic acid if a period of adaptation is allowed. So, increase the amounts fed slowly.

These plants also contain nitrites and nitrates which at times may well be responsible for lameness, acute scouring, abortions and death.

Furthermore, the fungus *aspergillus flavus* is known to produce oxalic acid when growing on straw, and this may be a cause of lameness in yarded animals.

189

Poisonous Plants

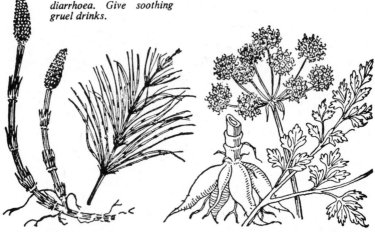

BRACKEN *is dealt with fully on page 186.*

BUTTERCUP *poisoning may occur in drought causing sore mouth (later, blisters and ulcers) and diarrhoea. Give soothing gruel drinks.*

HORSETAIL (*or snake-pipe*) *is dangerous green and in hay. Will cause diarrhoea, fall in milk yield and loss of condition. Give 1 pint (570 ml) of castor oil following by gruel drinks.*

WATER DROPWORT, *found in marshy places, will cause abdominal pain, diarrhoea, and possibly convulsions. Give 1 pint (570 ml) castor oil then gruel drinks.*

190

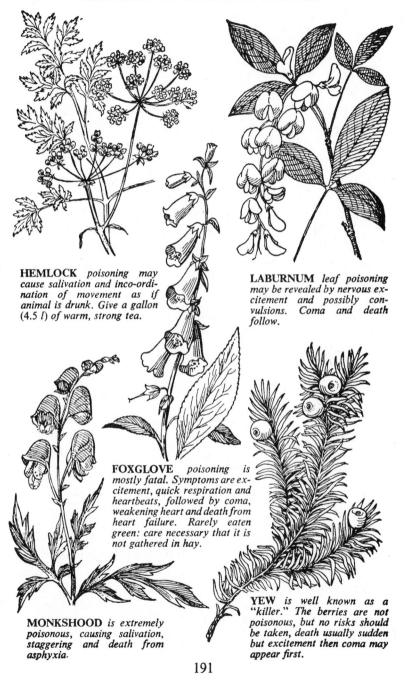

HEMLOCK *poisoning may cause salivation and inco-ordination of movement as if animal is drunk. Give a gallon (4.5 l) of warm, strong tea.*

LABURNUM *leaf poisoning may be revealed by nervous excitement and possibly convulsions. Coma and death follow.*

FOXGLOVE *poisoning is mostly fatal. Symptoms are excitement, quick respiration and heartbeats, followed by coma, weakening heart and death from heart failure. Rarely eaten green: care necessary that it is not gathered in hay.*

MONKSHOOD *is extremely poisonous, causing salivation, staggering and death from asphyxia.*

YEW *is well known as a "killer." The berries are not poisonous, but no risks should be taken, death usually sudden but excitement then coma may appear first.*

191

Black Scours

This is a condition also known as epidemic winter diarrhoea. It may occur in any part of the country from November to March. It runs a characteristic course. First, a few animals begin to scour violently and fall in milk yield. Then, while the first few are starting to tighten up and recover (they do this automatically in about seven days) others in the herd pick it up.

So it goes on, usually running right through the herd during a course of about three weeks in all.

The fact that recovery is automatic has led to many remedies being acclaimed as beneficial. It does seem, however, that bluestone (copper sulphate again) is a valuable remedy. The dose per animal should not exceed one drachm (1·08 g) – equivalent to a level teaspoonful – and this should not be repeated more than once during the course of any one month.

This should be done as soon as the outbreak starts. It should also be given to all contact animals, including the bull but not the calves. In this way the trouble can be cut short.

The cause of this disease is not known for certain, although American workers attribute it to a specific bowel organism known as *vibrio-duodenale* that can be transmitted experimentally to other animals.

In some outbreaks it appears that there is a predisposing cause such as the introduction of sugarbeet tops or sprouting roots, a sudden change of weather or a new consignment of feedingstuffs.

Salmonellosis

Whilst this disease has been widely recognised in calves, it is only of recent times that serious outbreaks in milking cows have been increasingly reported. The two common bacteria involved are *S. typhimurium* and *S. dublin*. The disease in adults usually appears during the summer months, whilst calves are more affected in the autumn. Either group can however be affected independently on the same farm without any spread from one to another.

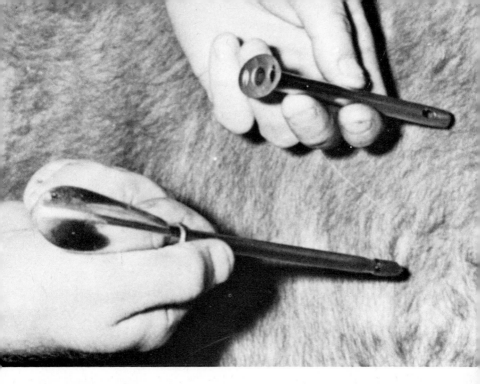

DEALING WITH BLOAT

The instruments used to relieve a cow from bloat are the trocar (punch) and canula (sleeve). The canula is fitted over the trocar for the puncture, then the trocar is withdrawn and the gas allowed to escape through the hollow canula.

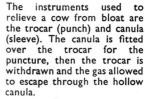

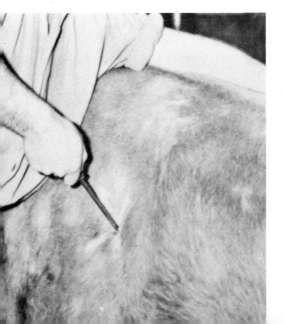

It is important to puncture the cow in the correct place. The point of the trocar and canula (or a knife will do) should be pushed down hard and at the angle shown. Keep the canula in until the vet arrives.

Paddock grazing—where the field is split into conveniently-sized blocks—is ousting strip-grazing as the most suitable system for intensively-stocked herds. It gives better control over grass intake and cuts down on soiling.

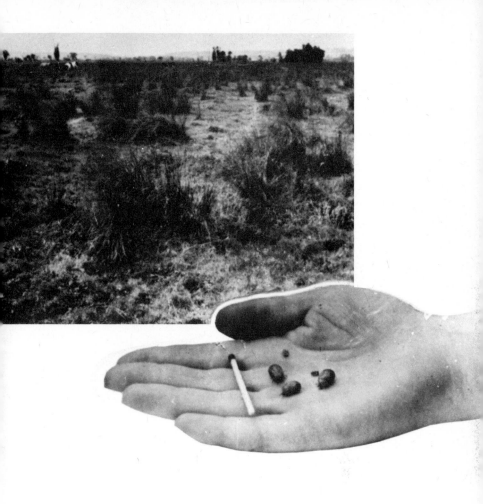

Ticks which cause redwater are shown in the hand above. Top picture illustrates typical tick-infested land. Clearing scrub and pasture improvement programmes help to eradicate the ticks.

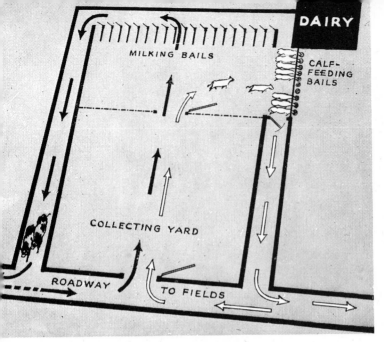

DAIRY

MILKING BAILS

CALF-FEEDING BAILS

COLLECTING YARD

ROADWAY

TO FIELDS

Typical time-saving milking and calf feeding layout employed in New Zealand. After the cows have been milked the calves are let in to milking yard and bails for feeding.

There is dysentery, a rise in temperature and a loss of flesh. Milk yield markedly declines and abortions may occur. Whilst many animals remain unthrifty, some develop arthritis or meningitis and continue to secrete the organisms. Calves, however, cease excreting the organisms on recovery. Death is not invariable but is usually sudden when it does occur.

There are no really effective control measures, but it is worthwhile taking faecal swabs to discover which animals are carriers. It must be born in mind that many such animals do not excrete the organisms or do so intermittently.

No clinical evidence of the disease is usually to be seen in a herd until a major stress factor is introduced. Then there may be signs of acute illness and abortions may start. Diagnosis is made difficult because blood levels of immune bodies may remain low and the organism may not even be found in the foetal material. It may occur, however, in faecal swabs later or at the time of the abortion. Abortions are usually isolated and do not occur in batches. Organisms can get into the milk and affect humans.

Stomach Worms

Lastly in this list of causes of scour in a number of animals at one time, I must deal with stomach worms.

Here, the key to diagnosis is the age of stock. Stomach worms are hardly likely to be responsible for scouring in a number of adult animals, *i.e.* over two years old. They could, however, be the cause if young stock are affected. For treatment and prevention in this case I refer you to chapter V.

WHEN ONE ANIMAL SCOURS

Now we come to individual cases of scour.

Here we can make two distinctions – the chronic type that gradually develops over a period and the acute type when you suddenly find one animal scouring like mad. In both cases the rest of the herd is probably perfectly all right.

The chronic type is the most straightforward for diagnosis. It will most likely be due to either Johne's disease or stomach worms.

In both cases the early symptoms may be similar – unthriftiness, a staring rusty coat and a dejected facial expression.
There may be a bubbly appearance to the dung in Johne's
disease.

Johne's Disease

I have previously discussed Johne's disease in particular when
referring to rearing young heifers. It is incurable. But if an
affected cow or heifer is taken in the early stages it may be
possible by the use of astringent medicines to keep her in
sufficiently good condition to fatten her or, if she is fairly well
forward in pregnancy, to allow her to produce a calf. Some
workers have reported good results in the control of this disease
by supplementing the diet with phosphorus or dressing the
pastures with phosphatic fertilisers.

In such circumstances it would be essential to keep the animal
strictly isolated to avoid spreading the infection about the farm
and premises. The dung should go only on arable land.

If the cow is kept till calving, special precautions should be
taken at that time. Her bearings should be washed down
thoroughly with disinfectant solution just before calving; the
calf should be taken from the cow at birth and the cow's teats
should be cleaned and disinfected before the calf is brought in to
suckle at each feed or before milk is taken from the cow for
bucket feeding.

However, if a cow found to be infected with Johne's disease
is of no great value I should advise you to have her slaughtered
immediately the presence of the disease is confirmed, or even
strongly suspected. By keeping her on the farm in the hope of
fattening her or getting her in calf you will be running a considerable risk of infecting other stock.

Although they occur, cases of congenital infection are very
rare and the observation made in one survey, that only one calf
in 158 was carrying Johne's disease bacilli, is of considerable
significance.

BLOOD TEST

A blood test has recently been developed which may yet be of considerable value in controlling this disease. The disadvantage of this, however, appears to be that it is somewhat difficult to interpret.

When the blood test is applied, animals affected with Johne's disease will, except possibly those in the advanced stages of scouring and emaciation, react positively, but so do many animals affected with the avian tubercle bacillus, and some which on slaughter show no signs of Johne's disease. This may be because they have, in fact, recovered from an attack. Nevertheless, despite its shortcomings, the blood test is still the most generally useful one available to provide a general overall picture, but it cannot be relied upon as a basis for elimination. Its adoption prevents the occurrence of clinical disease but does not appear to eradicate all infection if one can assume that the appearance of fresh blood reactors means fresh infections.

For the meantime, therefore, there is only one sure way of finding out whether chronic scouring is due to Johne's disease or stomach worms, and that is to have a laboratory examination made of dung samples and scrapings from the bowel walls. The latter is essential because the Johne's disease organisms may be present in the bowel wall and not in the dung.

If the dung examination reveals no significant organisms but only stomach worms, then a course of treatment may be advised. Here the manufacturer's instructions should be carefully followed, both with regard to size of and frequency of dose.

One further possible cause of chronic scouring is a tumour, abscess or abnormal growth, or occasionally the wooden-tongue fungus may be responsible for a bowel thickening and possibly a restriction.

Where a dung test reveals neither the presence of Johne's disease nor stomach worms then it might be worth while giving the animal a course of iodine drenches (as given for wooden tongue) followed by a course of sulphamezathine powders. A further safeguard would be to make sure that the mineral mixture used is well fortified with copper and cobalt.

A further possibility can be over-feeding of concentrates. This may happen in the case of a high-yielding cow needing a large amount of concentrates but being fed and milked only twice a day. Scouring in such circumstances would be accompanied by loss of condition and drop in yield.

Where it is essential to feed a large amount of cake to sustain yields, arrangements should be made to give the concentrates in at least three feeds, possibly four, to prevent indigestion and subsequent scouring. In general it is best to regard 9 lb (4 kg) of concentrates as the maximum a cow should have at each feed.

Urea is now widely used and provides a valuable form of cheap ammonia for the stomach flora to feed upon. A short period of acclimatisation is desirable to develop the proper bacterial flora. If maximum quantities of urea are introduced suddenly the excess ammonia will be absorbed, and there may well be scouring and a fall in milk yield.

IMPORTANCE OF DIAGNOSIS

You will now realise there are so many similarities occurring in the symptoms of all these that only a person with a wide experience of cattle troubles should be allowed to diagnose and prescribe in any such case. I assure you it is not always easy for him to hit the nail on the head first time.

For example, before a cow scours as a result of lead poisoning, she may stagger somewhat as in a milk fever or acetonaemia. Similarly there will be a rise in temperature in a case of salmonellosis and a rise in temperature in a case of chill. It will be of little avail if you prescribe Epsom salts in the former case; the animal would probably die because the correct remedy was not applied.

Thus your wisest course, if you value your stock, is to call for veterinary advice in any case where an individual animal starts to scour quite suddenly.

While you are waiting for this help you can take the cow's temperature; if it is above normal, you will do her a good turn by rugging her up, keeping her in a well-ventilated but draught-free spot and giving her a drench of one pint (570 ml) of warm oatmeal gruel.

Of course, it is wiser to try and prevent these things from happening than to tackle them when they do happen.

HOW MANAGEMENT COUNTS

This has turned out to be a long chapter.

Nevertheless, like most of the other chapters in this book, it can be boiled down to emphasising to you the importance of management, good management. Almost every digestive trouble that we have just discussed could be avoided in this way.

See that the cows' fodder is not placed where it can be splashed by dung; that's an important point in preventing infections, *e.g.* salmonellosis and Johne's disease. See that paint tins and old lino are not left lying about for cows to lick, *i.e.* avoid lead poisoning. See that any surplus mercury-dressed seed corn is not fed to stock; that's the way to avoid mercurial poisoning. See that no fertilisers are left about and that food does not get contaminated. Among other things, rats carry salmonella germs and leptospirosis parasites.

CHAPTER XIV

BLOAT AND OTHER GRAZING TROUBLES

CERTAIN grassland problems were dealt with in the previous chapter because they cause scouring. But that does not end the troubles arising from grazing.

The biggest headache here is bloat, also known as blown or hoven. Its technical name is *tympanites* and it really means an accumulation of a variety of gases in the rumen or first stomach of the cow.

Normally, such gases escape through the natural process of belching but, under certain conditions, the gases are formed too rapidly and become trapped in the unduly frothy contents so that they cannot escape in the usual way.

Consequently they inflate the affected part and considerably distend the abdomen, an appreciable swelling appearing on the left side and possibly extending above the level of the last rib and front edge of the pelvis.

MAY BE FATAL

If such a condition is not treated immediately, there is a grave risk of death from asphyxia and exhaustion owing to the pressure applied to the lungs and heart.

The advanced symptoms are well known. Affected cattle are usually considerably distended; they walk with difficulty or may be lying down outstretched. In the early stages the signs are usually these: standing still, appearing uncomfortable, stretching neck, looking depressed.

We now seem to be getting many more cases of blown than we used to. Further, we are getting more complicated cases – cases that are not put right by puncturing the animal to release the accumulated gases.

LINK WITH LEY FARMING

There is no doubt that this is connected with the greatly increased use of temporary leys on dairy farms.

That does not mean that we should condemn or even blame the system of ley farming. We have got to blame ourselves. The truth of the matter is that we have not yet learnt how to manage or feed the ley properly to avoid this trouble.

It is a job on which much research is being done.

However, the knowledge we now have enables us to recognise two types of bloat that occur when stock is grazing a new ley.

The first is the sub-acute type that results from turning out on to rapidly-growing grass.

The herbage is taken in quickly and in large quantities. Being young, it is rapidly broken down by bacteria in the first stomach. There is no fibre in it to retard the process and fermentation goes on at a tremendous rate.

ACUTE FORM

But there are additional factors. The increased rumenal pressure is sufficient to cause vascular and respiratory distress. Further, the gases are sometimes held in a thick frothy mass caused by soap-like substances in the herbage (saponins) and cannot readily escape even if the abdomen is punctured.

It is of considerable significance to learn from New Zealand work that the saliva itself contains substances which tend to create froth, so that increased appetite alone would tend to create adverse conditions in the rumen. This could explain why bloat occurs at the beginning of the growing season on permanent pastures also.

The second type is more acute. Cases are often characterised by the death of affected animals within 10 minutes to a few hours after first turning out.

We still do not know exactly what happens in these cases. But it has been shown that rapidly-growing grasses and certain clovers may contain substances that have a dangerous effect on stock.

Some clovers, for example, are known to possess a hydrocyanic acid-producing principle which is poisonous; others have been found to contain substances that paralyse the kind of muscle that is present in the stomach lining.

It may well be that these are the factors responsible for the sudden deaths.

Quite obviously the solution to these problems does not lie in advising you to buy a trocar and canula or to use a knife and puncture the animal.

In the sub-acute type, drenching an infected animal immediately with one pint (570 ml) of raw linseed oil and one ounce (28 g) of turpentine usually gives considerable relief.

With the frothy type of bloat special foam-reducing drenches based on silicones have proved successful in many cases; they can, if necessary, be administered directly into the rumen through the canula, or, where cows are known to be particularly susceptible it may be advisable to sprinkle a little peanut oil on to the dry food each morning before the animals are turned out. One to two ounces (28-56 g) of this or some bland oil like arachis will do. This can also be applied out of doors in appropriate quantities before cattle are turned out to eat the cut swath.

A further means of control is to administer a daily dose of 100 mg of penicillin. This controls the bacteria responsible for gas formation.

Indeed, as with all other cow troubles, that should be the aim with bloat: prevent it.

What is the best advice we can get on the subject?

First of all let us consider exactly what an animal does if it is turned out to grass, hungry and without any check on its actions and usually after being kept for months on hay and dry concentrates.

It will put its head down and graze solidly, without allowing itself time or opportunity to belch and release the accumulating gases.

Further, it will eat all the succulent young grasses that it can find and leave the coarse ones, instead of taking the rough with the smooth which would help to slow up fermentation.

Therefore it is a question of circumventing these natural animal tendencies.

METHODS OF CONTROL

Various ways have been suggested. They are:
1. To fence off an area – just sufficient for one day's grazing – and so force the animals to graze the sward close to the ground.
2. To keep the animals moving, so compelling them to raise their heads and encourage the elimination of the gases by belching. (This would need the services of an attendant).
3. To allow grazing for only a limited time, beginning with no more than twenty minutes night and morning and steadily extending its length as the animals get accustomed to the grass.
4. To curb the animals' appetites by feeding them with other food, preferably coarse fodder such as hay or straw, before turning them out. (If it is difficult to get the cattle to eat hay in the byre, try placing a few bales in the field on top of a few bales of straw; it is often more attractive this way).

There is yet a fifth suggestion, and that is strip grazing. It is to cut sufficient grass for a day's grazing and leave it to wilt before letting the cows eat it. Wilted grass seems to lose the dangerous qualities. A further safeguard is to spray the cut grass just before it is eaten with one of the new anti-foam mixtures,

201

Now I am not in favour of turning the cows into a field full of grass and fetching them off after a short time.

I feel that, this way, there is a danger in their realising that they have only a limited time and thus gorging ravenously in an attempt to eat their fill. That is, of course, just what we want to avoid.

To some extent the same thing happens where a limited area is given to the cows each day. Instead of tackling it steadily, they seem inclined to graze it as rapidly as possible.

But if a limited grazing area can be offered (enough, say, for 2-3 days) with a run-back to a byre or convenient place where hay or straw is available, then that may be the best practical solution. Any sense of urgency which may encourage gorging is thus removed.

Wiring off a portion of grass each day makes economic use of grass, while feeding a little long fodder has the same effect plus the advantage that it tends to balance the excess protein in the young grass.

If you will observe these rules, you will get far less trouble from bloat due to grazing, particularly when grazing young leys.

BLOAT FROM OTHER CAUSES

But we have still not dealt with bloat that occurs from causes other than grazing.

It may arise from general indigestion, from bad feeding, from choke, from abscess formation in the chest (due to metal foreign body), from impaction of food in the rumen or from lying on one side – as in milk fever.

Undoubtedly most of these could be prevented by good herd management. That, in fact, should be your aim.

Nevertheless cases do arise and they need prompt treatment. If the condition is mild, then a drench such as I have previously suggested will perhaps be all that is necessary. An additional help would be to walk the animal about or, at any rate, to stand her with her forequarters considerably higher than her rear-quarters, and give the gases a chance to escape naturally.

Placing a sack over the swelling and keeping it soaked with

cold water helps to reduce the swelling. Whilst there is still some "give" in the swelling there is still time, but if the animal has collapsed to the ground, the tongue protruding and is a bluish pallor about the membranes of the nose and mouth, no time must be lost. The only thing to do is to puncture the animal and release the gas.

PUNCTURING A BLOWN COW

To do this properly you must know (a) where to make the puncture and (b) how to make it.

Let's take "where" first.

Generally, it's the middle of the bulge. Another guide is to span the hand from the haunch bone to the last rib; the index finger will then point the spot.

As for "how", you can manage in an emergency with a pocket knife with a blade of from 4 inches to 8 inches (102-203 mm) in length. If that is all you have, pierce right through the skin and underlying tissues with it, then immediately twist the knife blade at right angles to the cut.

This twist is important. If you do not make it, the folds of skin will tend to cling to the knife blade and fail to release the gas properly. Then you may find the gas spreading under the skin.

Twisting the knife will create a clear passage for the gas to come through.

TROCAR AND CANULA

But here's the snag. Once you remove the knife, the edges of the cut will come together again and, if the rumen fermentation is unfinished, the cow will blow up once more.

That is why you really need a trocar and canula to deal properly with this kind of bloat.

Once the initial knife cut has been made (an inch-long (25 mm) cut is enough) the trocar and canula can be thrust into the rumen. Then withdraw the trocar and jeep the canula in position with a piece of tape or binder twine tied round the cow's belly.

You can leave it like that for a full day or more to ensure

that every bit of gas escapes. When you remove it, be careful to insert the trocar first to ensure that the instrument is cleanly withdrawn. Once the gas has ceased to bubble out freely you could pour some defoaming agent down the canula – in the absence of this some household detergent diluted 1:20 with warm water or one half pint (280 ml) of kerosene shaken up with an equal quantity of milk will help.

But, whether you give the first-aid treatment or not, I think it would be a good plan to call in professional aid in case of complications.

Redwater

Now let us get back to some of the other disease problems of grassland – poor grassland this time.

Redwater is one. Actually it is a parasitic disease, but it is so closely associated with grazing that this is the right place to deal with it.

It is due to a parasite conveyed by one of the common ticks, a blood-sucking insect that spends most of its life on the ground sheltering in the turf and soil crevices. This tick passes through a series of moults during two clearly defined periods of the year – March, April and May and again in August and September.

After each moult it climbs to the top of herbage shoots and attaches itself to passing animals, usually cows, sheep, hares and rabbits. There it gorges itself with blood and falls off to start the next moult.

No doubt you have seen these ticks on your cows, especially in the region of the groin, between the udder and thigh and inside the elbow – all places where the skin is thin.

Some ticks do not carry the redwater parasite; consequently, although you may find ticks on your stock, the disease will not necessarily occur.

But others, particularly in certain localities, carry the parasites and actually inject a few into the animal's blood stream at the same time as they inject something under the skin to stimulate the blood flow so that they can feed more easily.

Then the parasites multiply within the red blood cells of the cow and break them down, thus releasing into the urine the pigment that gives it its characteristic red or deep coffee colour.

NATURAL RESISTANCE

Cattle reared in redwater areas develop a natural resistance to the disease and do not often suffer from it, although calving may precipitate its occurrence. But an imported beast may become infected and suffer severely. It would probably die if not treated.

There is, however, a specific remedy for the disease. It can be given by your veterinary surgeon and he should be told immediately the first symptoms appear.

The cow will lose appetite and will not cud. Her nose may be poked out, her pulse weak and rapid. The heart will beat rapidly and is often audible; temperature will be high. The urine will be coloured, the milk may be pink.

In the early stages of the disease there will be "pipe-stem" diarrhoea, but this is soon followed by a marked foul-smelling constipation.

AIM AT ELIMINATION

It is not easy to suggest how the disease can be completely eliminated. If draining, liming and proper cultivation of the affected areas is possible, that will get rid of the ticks. But many affected areas are in situations where this is impossible.

The second best line of attack is to keep down scrub growth – grass, briars and brambles – as much as possible by burning in August and September. Rabbits and hares should also be destroyed.

Further, it should be made a common practice during the tick seasons to remove ticks from the cattle at milking time. Scrape them off into a tin of paraffin. If they are difficult to move, dab them first with a little paraffin. That will weaken their hold.

In any redwater area it is advisable to have young stock brought in and injected immediately a case occurs. This is a curative remedy. So far there is no satisfactory method of protective vaccination.

Blood infection by another parasite transmitted by the common tick has been occasionally reported in dairy herds in recent times. There is a dramatic drop in milk production, and most cows run a high temperature lasting for up to three weeks. This may escape diagnosis for some time because the urine remains normal.

Liver Fluke

Fortunately liver fluke trouble is not nearly so common in cattle as it is in sheep. But it does occur more often than supposed and should be suspected if animals show signs of scouring when put on a low-lying pasture or when the milk yield of a number of animals unaccountably falls.

Liver fluke infection of the cow (or sheep) occurs when these animals are brought into contact with certain minute snails which harbour the fluke during part of their life cycle. These are usually found on moist land.

It is possible to get rid of the trouble by destroying the snails on the pasture and this can be done by broadcasting a powder made up of six parts white sand to one part copper sulphate.

Dressing rate should be from 1½ cwt to 2½ cwt per acre (189-282 kg/ha); application is best made between mid-July and end of September. Stock should be kept off the pasture until the dressing has been well washed in by rain.

Infected cattle can be successfully treated with hexachlorethane* and can be kept free from the disease by regular dosing with it; but every effort should be made to destroy the snails as dosing is expensive in materials and time.

The fluke is the same as that which affects sheep therefore sheep pastures can be dangerous. An inspection of carcases at slaughter will tell you whether fluke is present or not.

Grass Staggers

This I have already dealt with in detail and I refer you to the discussion in chapter IX.

---

* *There are several other good remedies now on the market.*

But here I would stress again the risk of not feeding cattle when they are grazing rapidly-growing herbage promoted by nitrogenous dressings.

If, in such circumstances, cows are given some supplementary feeding – a starchy, mineralised food with some calcined magnesite – they are much less likely to go down with grass staggers.

Other valuable safeguards against this trouble are: 1. feeding well in winter, especially with good quality hay and silage; 2. having some foggage grazing available in winter to avoid too sudden a change in food when the early bite is ready; 3. controlled grazing in spring to avoid sudden variations in feed quality; 4. providing extra food and shelter in wet, cold weather.

MANAGING THE LEY

Let me sum up this chapter by returning to the question of ley versus permanent pasture.

From the veterinary point of view I am all in favour of new leys, of taking the plough round the farm.

Look what that will get rid of – Johne's disease bacilli, tb bacilli, coccidia, husk worm larvae and stomach worm larvae – to mention only a few of the troubles that dairy farmers have to contend with in those old pastures.

It may be true that new leys are not themselves trouble-free. But we must not condemn them because cases of bloat and mineral disturbances arise. These occur simply because we have not yet appreciated the deficiencies which may arise.

There is a job for scientists and farmers to do together. It will lead to even higher production and better animal health.

CHAPTER XV

DEALING WITH MISCELLANEOUS TROUBLES

FORTUNATELY there are not many of these. Even more fortunately the majority are either rare – like lock-jaw – or are not too serious – like lice.

But they nearly all have one thing in common; most of them can be avoided by good management on the farm.

Lock-Jaw

This is the common name for tetanus, a disease caused by a bacterium known as *Clostridium tetani* which, when present in dirty wounds where there is little or no free oxygen, produces a nerve "toxin" or poison. This stimulates the nerves which keep the voluntary muscles of the body in a constant state of contraction or "tetany."

The germ seems to be either particularly virile or especially concentrated in the soil in certain areas. In some districts, certain fields only may be infected and have a bad local reputation for the disease.

Fortunately, cows seldom suffer from it. Nevertheless proper attention to wounds when they occur will help to prevent lock-jaw setting in, and for this I refer you to the next chapter on first-aid.

LUMPY JAW

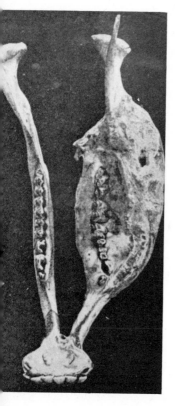

Above, affected cow; left, jaw bones
showing the effect this disease has.

WOODEN TONGUE

The coarsened and lignified section of
affected tongue is shown on the left of
this photograph.

These photographs are published by
permission of Iodine Educational Bureau.

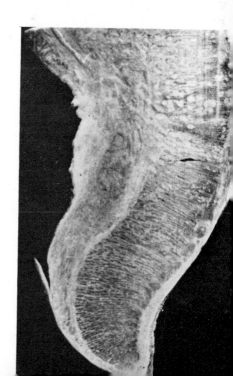

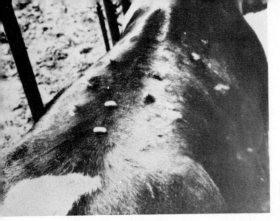

DEALING WITH
WARBLE FLY

Top picture shows a cow badly infected with warbles. Inset, a warble grub about to emerge.

The method of warble prevention is well known—regular treatment (using hard scrubbing brush) with a proprietary solution.

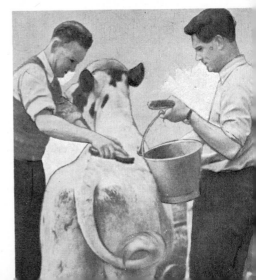

Should a case occur, you will recognise it by the fact that the animal will move exceedingly stiffly and will not be able to lift up its legs. The inner eyelids may flash across when startled or remain half across the eye.

An affected animal will need veterinary treatment but, while waiting for it, try to get the animal into a dark box and keep it perfectly quiet. The bedding should be as short as possible to avoid handicapping the patient in its movements. Chaff is most suitable.

Food may have to be given in gruel form if the animal is not able to feed itself. You will find that it will, in such a case, quickly learn how to suck up the gruel.

Wooden Tongue and Lumpy Jaw

Both these conditions are caused by a type of fungus.

In one, the soft tissues of the head – such as the tongue and cheek – are attacked; the responsible organism in this case being known as *actinobacillus lignierise*. In the other, the bones of the head and jaw are involved; here the organism is called *actinomyces bovis*.

Hence the two name distinctions – wooden tongue and lumpy jaw.

In the very early stages of wooden tongue there will be a slight dribbling. If that is spotted, then an examination of the raised platform at the back of the tongue (the dorsum) may reveal the irregularly distributed orange-coloured patches which are typical of wooden tongue.

This back portion of the tongue is the part usually affected though any part may become involved.

In the later stages of the disease there will be marked slobbering, the mouth being held slightly open. This gets steadily worse, the tongue becomes swollen and hard and tends to protrude; little yellowish ulcers appear.

Because of the difficulty of eating, the animal becomes emaciated.

There is, however, a remedy that is usually very effective.

This is the well-known wooden-tongue mixture. It should be started immediately the first symptoms are noticed.

Should a case not respond to this treatment your vet may try an injection of sodium iodide, although this involves a certain amount of risk of the animal relapsing from shock or, if in-calf, aborting.

In lumpy jaw, the bones are eroded. There is cavity formation and enlargement, the skin over the bone breaking and liberating pus.

Here, the prospects of complete recovery are poor. If the animal has a good carcase value I should be inclined to advise you to sell it while it is in good condition. If you wish to persevere, then the iodine medicine should be given as for wooden tongue.

Better still, call in your vet; he may try an intravenous injection of sodium iodide. But I would not hold out very high hopes of success.

This is one of the very few instances in which I cannot say "prevention is better than cure". I wish I could but, unfortunately, the fungi responsible are so widely distributed about the farm, especially in hay and straw, that it is an almost impossible task to protect stock from the risk of infection.

Barley straw seems to have a greater reputation than other long fodders for carrying the fungi but it may well be that barley awns cut or graze the interior of the mouth and thus opened the way for the infection they may carry.

A lump on the side of an animal's face can be caused by an abscess under one of the teeth, involving the jawbone. It is quite common for such an abscess to develop under a tooth in a young calf and subsequently to leave a permanent lump even when the abscess is no longer active. But, by then, the lump will be too hard and bony for any treatment to be effective.

Bottle Jaw

Sometimes cattle develop swellings under the jaw, a condition known as "bottle jaw".

This is due to an accumulation of fluid between the jaw bones and indicates an advanced stage of malnutrition. It occurs wherever there is semi-starvation, irrespective of whether this is due to actual lack of food or a debilitating disease.

The distinction between this and lumpy jaw (apart from the fact that bottle jaw is associated with emaciation) is that the lumpy jaw swelling is persistent and hard whereas the bottle jaw swelling is flabby and tends to appear, disappear, and re-appear according to the state of health of the animal. This condition is encountered in Johne's disease, fluke infestation, parasitism and ragwort poisoning.

WHAT SLOBBERING MAY MEAN

Slobbering, although a symptom of wooden tongue, may well be an indication of other troubles which should be diagnosed and put right as soon as possible.

For example, a loose tooth or a foreign body in the gum, causing pain and possibly an abscess, would almost certainly give rise to slobbering.

So, where a case is clearly not one of wooden tongue, it would be well to call in veterinary advice as infection of the teeth, palate, or salivary glands may be involved and sulpha drugs or antibiotics may be necessary. And remember, this symptom is one of the earliest signs of foot-and-mouth disease.

Haematoma

Haematoma is the name given to a blood tumour caused by the rupturing of blood vessels under the skin and the formation of a "pool" of blood which remains trapped and steadily hardens.

A true haematoma is generally best left alone as ultimately the hardened blood is re-absorbed into the system.

But if you find a lump – which can be alarmingly large in size – which does not clear up it is only wise to seek veterinary advice about it in case it may be due to damage or a foreign body, either of which can have caused infection of the tissues. It might even be a rupture or hernia which it would clearly be unwise to cut with a knife.

211

Nodular Necrosis

This is a condition in which walnut-sized lumps appear in the muscles and show through the skin. They are not attached to the skin and are firm to the touch. They can occur anywhere on the body but are most common under the root of the tail and down the buttocks.

It is possible that these can be confused with skin tb in the early stages; therefore veterinary diagnosis is advisable. But there is no satisfactory treatment for nodular necrosis.

Ear Infection

If an animal is seen holding its head on one side, ear trouble can be suspected – especially if a brownish discharge can be seen inside the ear.

The trouble can usually be cleared up by moistening a piece of cotton wool with hydrogen peroxide, twisting it round the handle of a wooden spoon and gently cleaning the ear out with it while the animal's head is held by an assistant.

After cleaning out in this way drop into the ear some 5 per cent iodoform powder – about a teaspoonful. Repeat this treatment daily for about a week. A hanging ear can follow lightning strike.

Listerellosis

In America cases of abortion and death in cattle associated with an organism known as *Erysipelothrix monocytogenes* have frequently been reported, but such conditions are rare in the British Isles.

The small organism attacks the nervous system. Infected animals show loss of appetite, marked salivation, head held low and to one side, with a general appearance of depression and a staggering gait with a tendency to move in circles. Slaughter is generally necessary.

Aujeszky's Disease

This virus disease, best known amongst pigs in Europe, was first recognised in Great Britain in 1938. Whilst it is characterised in the pig by a transient febrile condition, in cattle it is associated with intense irritation which is responsible for the name "mad itch".

Animals rub and bite themselves furiously and become progressively weaker before death.

"Q" Fever

The rickettsial bodies (*Coxiella burnetti*) responsible for this disease in the human are carried by the cow and conveyed to the former on drinking infected milk. Cows show no symptoms but humans suffer from respiratory distress and a high fluctuating temperature for 3-4 weeks but with no marked lung congestion.

It is well known in cattle in Australia where it is thought to be transmitted by the droppings of blood-sucking ticks, but the source of infection in the U.K. is not known.

Foul-in-the-Foot

It is quite common for one or two cows in a herd to suffer from this condition.

Generally it begins as a small corn between the claws. This enlarges and tends to force the claws apart. It is very painful.

If left unchecked, a core forms which can be removed – if you can persuade the patient to keep still while the operation is being performed. But if left to take its course the animal will lose a lot of flesh.

Originally it was a case of poulticing with antiphlogistine, kaolin or bran to draw out the core, after which the hole was packed with boracic-iodoform powder and well covered. Now we have a more simple and effective remedy in the intravenous injection of one of the M & B preparations which your practitioner can give.

Many cases of foul are caused by the sharp edges of coarse grasses being drawn between the claws. This is most common in wet weather in summer.

VALUE OF FOOTBATH

In particularly stubborn cases the veterinary treatment may be aided by cleaning between the claws of the affected foot and packing the gap firmly with an antiseptic ointment or powder.

Cover the dressing with tow and bandage. Inspect the foot in a week's time; then clean with soap and water and repeat if necessary.

Where the trouble is prevalent on the farm it is wise to build a footbath for the herd to pass through before and after milking and also to avoid as far as possible having to drive the cows through muddy gateways and lanes where there are many stones.

The footbath, which should have a ribbed bottom to open out the claws, should contain a 5 per cent bluestone solution, renewed weekly in wet, dirty weather, fortnightly at other times. To reduce soil contaminations a clean approach of at least 20 yards (18 m) should be arranged. As bluestone is poisonous, the footbath is best covered to prevent young stock and even domestic animals from drinking it.

When cows are outwintered in particularly wet and dirty weather (and especially on flinty and stony soils) it is a good plan to hose down their legs and feet when they come into the sheds to be milked.

Footrot

Footrot differs from foul-in-the-foot in that it involves the horn and not the tissue.

The first sign of it is lameness. On closer inspection there will be found under the horny sole of the foot a black, foul-smelling, thick fluid; the horn will be soft and crumbly.

Cleaning up the horn and removing any surplus sole (so that infected parts are exposed to the air) should rapidly clear up the condition. Application of Stockholm tar or a propamadine-type of cream will help. Chloromycetin sprays are now proving valuable; Crystal Violet is incorporated.

Pastures infected with the footrot virus should be clear of infection after two or three weeks' rest.

Pink Heel

This arises from over-feeding concentrates – not necessarily in total quantity but in amount per feed. The result is a characteristic pink blush or patchiness of the heels of the hind feet, possibly associated with restlessness and slight paddling.

The remedy is to cut down concentrate feeding, to give a drench of 12 ounces (340 g) of Epsom salts in 1½ pints (0·85 l) of water and to allow the affected animal as much hay as she will clear up in three feeds per day of about twenty minutes each.

The method of prevention is, of course, to avoid over-feeding at any one meal. Bear in mind the point I have previously made – that a limit of from 8 to 10 lb (3·62 - 4·54 kg) of concentrates (according to breed and size of cow) is the maximum amount a cow is able to eat at a meal and still have an appetite for hay or silage.

Therefore the total daily concentrate requirements should be fed over a sufficient number of meals to avoid exceeding the maximum at any one time.

Paddling and marked discomfort due to laminitis (or congestion of the blood vessels within the hooves) is occasionally seen in heavy-milking cows at the peak of lactation, especially in Friesians.

This condition may be confused with what is known in some parts of the country as "milk lameness". High-yielding cows are mostly affected, showing hip lameness. This is associated with low blood phosphorus and is attributed to the fact that intake of herbage and other foods is not adequate enough to meet the needs of milk production. Half-an-ounce (14 g) of steam bone flour per day usually brings about considerable improvement and blood phosphorus levels rise.

A condition resembling laminitis is also occasionally encountered in young beef animals kept indoors. Congestion appears to be encouraged when the bedding becomes very soft and "mushy", and the weather conditions are warm at the same time.

Tetanus

This disease, better known in humans as "lockjaw", is not

215

uncommon in cattle but may be overlooked as the early symptoms of mild bloat may be all that is to be seen. In characteristic cases, however, the gait may be unsteady due to stiff joints and the eyes may roll about in a distinctive way.

The condition is brought about by the production of a toxin by a germ known as *Clostridium tetani*. This is widely distributed in the soil and so may get into wounds. It, however, only grows in the absence of oxygen so does not function readily where wounds are kept clean. Treatment is not always successful, but where the disease is a problem on the farm, it is worth anticipating trouble and vaccinating all the stock with a mixed welchii/tetanus vaccine.

Problems Associated with Slurry

The use of slurry on pastures from whatever source – cattle, pigs, poultry or humans (sewage) – presents certain hazards to livestock. Cattle may be exposed to Johne's bacilli transmitted in bovine slurry, salmonella organisms such as *S. dublin*, *S. typhimurium*, *S. typhi* and possibly copper poisoning, in association with the spreading of pig slurry.

Salmonella organisms may also be distributed in poultry manure. Human sewage may carry these organisms and also those of tuberculosis. But apart from copper which, of course, remains permanently in the ground, where taken up by the herbage it increases the intake by grazing, the organisms mentioned are all likely to die out well before six months have passed.

With the exception of the Johne's disease organism, it is probable that most of the others, especially the viruses, are very quickly destroyed where slurry is stored for brief periods of a few weeks before distribution. This is a different situation to that where the dung is moved direct from the environment of the animals and put directly on the pastures.

Teat Sores and Allied Skin Conditions

The common skin conditions affecting the teat and udder of the dairy cow in the UK today are:

Virus Infections—Cowpox and vaccinia, pseudo-cowpox, bovine herpes mammillitis and papillomatosis (warts).

Bacterial and Fungal Infections—Mycotic dermatitis, ringworm and an infection with an acid-fast bacillus.

Differentiation of these conditions needs considerable experience, especially as they often resemble one another at different stages of infection.

COWPOX. Closely allied to the other pox viruses, that of cowpox has been known since the beginning of the last century. It is widely distributed throughout the world though rarely seen in Europe and North America.

In man the virus causes milkers' nodules. In the cow it is a mildly contagious disease of the teats and udder, occasionally appearing as an isolated sore on other parts of the body. Both in man and animals the incubation period is five days and associated with a slight fever. There is early tenderness of the teats, udder and skin followed by the appearance of roughly circular, reddish areas, in the centre of which a pale yellow or white papule develops. In a few days this has become hardened and suppurative. The vesicle ruptures leaving a red, tacky scab. Healing proceeds from the centre only and takes about three weeks, some small, inverted scars being eventually left.

Immunity is said to last the life of the animal, and any human victim achieves a high degree of resistance to smallpox lasting several years at least.

PSEUDO-COWPOX. The incubation period is six days but there is no rise in temperature to herald the appearance of the teat sores. A reddish, swollen area may be seen which is quickly covered by a sticky exudate and the teat is tender to the touch. The inflamed area becomes dry and scabs over. Healing soon commences, beginning from the centre until a very characteristic ring or horse-shoe-shaped crusty ridge remains. Whilst the process may repeat itself on other parts of the teat in the absence of any immunity, the damage is very superficial and no scar is left.

Variable forms are common which make diagnosis difficult. The whole teat may be involved especially in heifers, or the lower teat and orifice alone, this area becoming covered with black scabs. Muzzle sores may be seen in calves suckling infected dams. The latter is correctly referred to as bovine papular stomatitis.

BOVINE HERPES MAMMILLITIS. This condition, although widespread in the UK, has only of recent times assumed importance and caused increasing economic loss. It is much more severe than the pox diseases and whilst there are no systemic effects, large areas of the udders as well as the teats are usually involved. Painful, oedematous swellings first appear on the teats followed by vesicles which rupture and exudation quickly follows. Scabbing then occurs, but the healing process which takes place underneath may not be complete for up to 10 weeks. Milking delays the process and a sore granulating area develops. Sometimes considerable skin areas peal off, that of the teat coming away like a thimble. In newly calved heifers the skin between the thighs may become involved and muzzle infections become established before recovery and lasting immunity finally occur.

WISE PRECAUTIONS

Your aim should be to prevent an outbreak by good hygienic methods, avoiding chaps and always having hands washed and equipment sterilised. Calves should not be allowed to suckle affected cows.

Precautions to take if it occurs are as follows:

Milk the infected cow or cows last, preferably by hand and by a person who will not handle the rest of the herd. The sores are extremely resistant to any kind of treatment, but you should try smearing them with penicillin cream on two successive days; then rub the cream off gently with a clean dry cloth and apply sulphathiazole cream.

Correct diagnosis is not always easy and professional advice will be worthwhile. There appears to be some immunity following, but a second attack may follow soon after the disappearance of recently-healed sores.

Black Spot

A hardening of the skin round the teat orifice is the first

indication of this troublesome complaint caused by *Fusiformis necrophorus.*

It most probably follows some injury at this point caused either by biting flies, friction with floors or bedding when lying down or bad milking methods (such as leaving the teat cups on too long); then bacteria get in and make things worse.

Early treatment is essential. The scab should be softened first by immersing the teat in a warm 10 per cent dettol solution with bicarbonate of soda added at the rate of a heaped tea-spoonful to each pint of solution.

Remove as much of the scab as possible, then thoroughly dry the teat before applying penicillin cream. The application of chloromycetin spray is also effective.

Hand milking may be necessary or complete cessation for a week. If the sore is very serious, drying-off the quarter may be the only course to take. This should return to normal next lactation.

The term "Black Spot" is also applied to a condition which may arise if the air holes in the pulsators become blocked so interfering with the rhythmic collapse of the liners. As the basic cause is mechanical, quite a number of animals could be affected thus distinguishing the condition from the foregoing type associated with *F. necrophorus.* And again the risk of over-milking causing initial necrosis should be remembered.

Sores on Teats

Sores on teats which are neither cowpox nor black spot frequently arise. Many of them that occur at the base of the teat and on the skin of the udder are associated with fungi rather like the ringworm fungus. They are highly resistant to treatment.

You can try the following:

Clean the sores and surrounding area with warm soap and water. If the scabs come off fairly easily, remove them. Then apply with a paint brush to the sores and the skin round about a gentian violet solution of which you can buy a few ounces (grams) from your veterinary chemist. The new fungicidal sprays are also worth trying.

Cracked Teats

Cracked teats occur both in winter and in summer.

They are often particularly troublesome on account of soreness and bleeding and the difficulty of milking.

The best way of tackling this trouble is to dry the teats thoroughly after each milking and to smear them with an ointment incorporating cod-liver oil in a zinc oxide or magnesium carbonate base. This can be made up by any chemist.

At all costs avoid turning cows out into a dirty, muddy yard or lane so that their udders are fouled before they reach their grazing. In summer it may help to apply a fly repellent spray to either side of the udder before turning the cows out.

Always make sure that udder-washing disinfectant solution is at the right strength.

Pea in Teat

The fairly common complaint of a "pea in the teat" is found most frequently in freshly-calved cows. The "pea" consists of a flap of tissue or a thickening of the surface so forming a protuberance that the free passage of milk down the teat canal is interfered with. Sometimes there is a membrane stretching right across. This makes milking difficult, whether by hand or machine.

Removal of this obstruction should be left to a veterinary surgeon. The "pea" has generally to be removed surgically.

Milk Fistula

A milk fistula is an opening from the teat canal to the skin at the side of the teat, and may be the result of a bad tear. It interferes with milking, particularly hand milking. Its presence may also facilitate the entry of mastitis organisms – especially if there is a tendency for milk to run even when the animal is not being milked.

The use of collodion or plasters is rarely satisfactory. The best means of tackling the problem is a surgical operation when the cow is dry. This your veterinary surgeon will do by cutting the edges of the hole to create a raw surface and then stitching them together so that they will unite.

Warts

An old-fashioned remedy for getting rid of a wart was to tie a bit of horsehair round it and gradually tighten it up until the wart dropped off. It used to work – provided you could get the horsehair round the wart!

Today they are dealt with more simply. With the cylindrical ones hanging from the teats or udder as though fastened on a stalk all you need to do is to grasp each one firmly between the tip of your thumb and finger and give a slight but quick snatch. A little bleeding may follow but can be ignored.

FORMS OF TREATMENT

Round and flat warts round the teat and udder are not so easily dealt with.

You can try rubbing them with a stick of caustic silver until each one bleeds; or you can apply a dressing of a mixture of $\frac{1}{2}$ ounce (14 g) salicylic acid and 2 ounces (57 g) of collodion flexile.

But the modern veterinary treatment is to give an injection of an antimony preparation known as anthiomaline. The best results are claimed to be obtained from intramuscular injections of 15 cc given on from four to six occasions at intervals of 48 hours.

After this treatment the warts become quite crumbly and rub off easily.

PREVENTING INFECTION

No one yet knows how to prevent warts but attempts are now being made to prepare a vaccine against them. It is thought by some that they are encouraged by a mineral deficiency, but there is no evidence to prove that. We do know, however, that they are infectious; and are more likely to be caused by a virus that can be passed from cow to cow.

So, where the proper hygienic precautions are taken in handling stock at milking time, there should not be much fear of spreading wart infection.

Angleberries

These you can ignore. They hang from the belly and sometimes from the neck like thin grey cords, but they will drop off when the affected animals moult in spring. As they are wart-like in nature you could have the anthiomaline treatment carried out if you wish.

Both warts and angleberries are forms of what are known as papillomas – quite a distinctive type of tissue growth. They are generally benign but may appear in awkward situations such as the tip of the penis or in the oesophagus. Where it is difficult to deal with them by the methods already referred to, it is possible to employ an autogenous vaccine.

Warbles

If every farmer conscientiously treated all his stock over three months old in accordance with the Warble Fly Dressing Order, there would be no need to refer to the problem in this book. As it is, we still have the problem in spite of the fact that farmers know they lose money through it. They get less milk in the fly season, and hides are often extensively damaged by the warble larvae and so made less valuable as leather.

The difficulty is that the fly which only lives a few days cannot be attacked. You have to wait for the right stages in the life cycle before being sure of a kill. The fly lays its eggs in groups on the hairs of the belly and legs. Grubs hatch out, pierce the skin and migrate through the body to the back via the nerves and spinal cord. It is these over-wintering grubs which can and should be destroyed by the application of an organo-phosphorus liquid preparation to the skin of the back. No rubbing is necessary. (Gloves and overall MUST be worn by the operator.)

The liquid penetrates into the body and kills 95 per cent of the larvae. This treatment is best carried out between September 15th and November 30th. If some grubs are observed to have survived and are pushing up the skin of the back, a second treatment should be carried out in March; in fact, this is compulsory by law. But no treatment should ever be carried out between December 1st and the middle of March when the larvae are established in the gullet wall. If it is, the effects may be serious.

The previous year's flies will all have died and you will have prevented the current year's crop from developing. And as the warble fly has a rather limited range of flight, you probably won't even be troubled with it coming from your neighbours' farm unless your stock get very close to his. The flies don't like crossing water or flying in woodland. So, to sum up: Autumn dressing will mean fewer affected cattle in the spring, coupled with a minimum milk loss plus improved weight gain and carcase value.

N.B. Never attempt to squeeze out a grub from the back unless you are sure of getting it out without it bursting.

Mange

If cattle show an irregular loss of hair with crusty scabs over small areas that enlarge but slowly and are very itchy when rubbed, then the trouble is likely to be mange. The affliction is becoming more common in this country.

Because we now know that the responsible acari or mites are relatively sparsely distributed over the skin very careful examination of skin scrapings is necessary to determine the presence of these mites. Effective mange dressings are now available.

Lice

Really, these are a sign of bad management or bad housing – which comes to the same thing.

In these days of gammexane and other suitable preparations those ugly bare patches on the sides of the neck, along the back and at the root of the tail that used to be commonly seen a few years ago, particularly after a winter's housing, should never appear.

The louse – there are three species occurring in cattle – spends its whole life on the animal and does not fall off to moult or lay eggs. So, spraying or dusting will destroy the lice and the grubs that hatch from their eggs. If the job is repeated at 10-day intervals during the winter, there should be no re-infection.

It's a simple job but well worth doing. The irritation from lice is not a pleasant thing for cattle to suffer. At the least it will create sufficient discomfort to cause a reduced yield or retarded development in the case of youngsters.

Treatment consists of thorough spraying of the greater part of the body of the affected animal with an appropriate gammex-ane spray. Especially is it necessary to spray the sore parts well; the ears must also be swabbed out as the parasites hide in these places and cause re-infection later.

OTHER CAUSES OF HAIR LOSS

Sometimes cattle suffer loss of hair, often quite extensively, even when lice or mange are not the cause. A condition of this kind may be associated with a thick yellow scurf on the skin which comes away with the hair when scraped, leaving a raw wound.

This may be due to a disturbance of the vitamin A meta-bolism or to a contamination of the skin with crude oil due to animals rubbing against or licking machinery heavily coated with oil or grease.

An affected animal may be given a dose of one pint (570 ml) of cod-liver oil. If it is a herd problem, then a group of animals can be tried with 2 ounces (57 g) of yeast daily for each beast, and vitamin A and D supplement added to their rations.

If this is successful the rest of the herd can be treated similarly.

Nettlerash or "Blain" (see also Anaphyaxis)

In this condition, areas of the skin – especially about the face and throat – suddenly become raised in weals or blisters. As far as we know this is probably due to the sensitivity of the indi-vidual animal to some form of protein.

The first symptoms are uneasiness and perspiration, followed by nervous excitement. If the swellings are near the eyes, the animal may be unable to see. If they are round the throat – either inside or outside – there may be snoring and difficulty in breathing.

In extreme cases it may be necessary to grasp the tongue and hold it at the side of the mouth until professional help is available to make an opening in the windpipe through which the animal can breathe.

Calamine lotion should be applied externally. Where it can be given, a drench of 1 lb (454 g) of Epsom salts in 2 pints (1·14 l) of cold water is useful.

Stop feeding any long fodder and give succulent, laxative food such as grass, silage, mangolds, etc.

Fluorine Poisoning

When lameness and joint troubles occur in industrial areas, especially on farms on the windward side of brick factories and iron foundries and those engaged in certain other activities, the possibility of fluorine poisoning should not be overlooked.

Some clays and certain materials used as fluxes may contain the dangerous element which is volatilised and distributed in the flue gases over a large area. It is deposited on vegetation to which cattle have access, but is not absorbed into the plant as such.

Young growing animals are most susceptible to an increased intake of this mineral. Their teeth become mottled and their bones thickened and knobbly. Where the outgrowths occur around a joint, movement becomes restricted and painful.

Although fluorine is only absorbed with difficulty, continuous exposure to it results in the deposition of appreciable quantities in the bony skeleton, the remainder being liberated in the urine.

Once an animal has become affected there is no cure. All that you can do is to avoid grazing your animals in fields that may have become contaminated. Any arable crops you grow in these fields will not be affected and can be safely fed to stock, if collected after heavy rain, or first sprayed with a hose.

Purchased adult stock are unlikely to be affected because the growth of the skeleton is complete; therefore a good plan on such farms is to sell off calves as they are born and buy in-milk cows for herd replacements.

It is now possible to put in scrubbers in the furnaces so removing fluorine from the flue gases. In other circumstances the land is often bought by the company responsible for ths contamination and let at a reduced rent in view of the hazarde involved.

Windgalls

The cause of windgalls (soft swellings on legs) is not clearly understood. In horses, overwork, strain and bad conformation are likely explanations.

Should this trouble occur with cattle it can best be treated by applying to the swelling a wad of wool waste or felt and bandaging this on quite firmly so that direct pressure is brought to bear on the swelling.

Every half hour or so cold water should be poured onto the bandage. Alternatively a hose-pipe can be tied on so that the bandage is continuously irrigated for about an hour three or four times a day.

If this gives no satisfactory improvement within two weeks, a blister should be applied.

CHAPTER XVI

CASTRATING, BULL-RINGING AND DEHORNING

ON many store-raising farms, particularly in the upland areas, the castration of bull calves has been a normal practice for many years and the technique is well understood.

But with the growing development of beef production as a side-line on many dairy farms – even though the beef animals may not be fattened on the farm where they are born – there is a need to have the technique explained.

Castration is a job that wants doing properly; otherwise there is a risk that the animal may remain fertile with consequent serious monetary loss on the beast itself and on any beef heifers which may have been running with it and have been got in-calf by it.

OPERATION IS BEST

Undoubtedly the best method in most cases is surgical removal. It is sure. Further, in the long run, I believe it causes less pain. The soreness after surgical removal lasts only for a brief period; after the bloodless method the animal is dull and walks uncomfortably sometimes for as long as three or four days.

Castration is best performed when the calves are three months old, but it can be done at from two to four months. I would not recommend it earlier than two months because, if done too young, there is a danger of the substance of the testicle shelling out and the epididymis slipping out of reach.

WHEN TO USE CASTRATOR

The use of the bloodless method of castration is certainly worth considering when fly conditions are bad during the late summer and there is a risk of a wound becoming fly-blown; also, during extreme cold weather, when the shock of a surgical operation is best avoided. And I would probably advise it when I see that the calves involved were herded in small dirty premises; in such circumstances there would be a risk of wound infection.

So it is well worth knowing how the job can be done to ensure that mistakes are kept to a minimum.

The first thing is to understand the principle of the method. It is that the artery in each cord is so compressed that the two inner sides heal together and prevent the flow of blood on which the testicles depend.

Degeneration of the testicles then follows.

BUYING A CASTRATOR

The next thing is to have the right instrument for the job. Here it is important to keep in mind that if only a fraction of either cord escapes the compression of the jaws, some blood supply may reach the testicle and maintain bull behaviour; it may even be possible for sperms to be ejaculated.

So choose a variety of bloodless castrators that has a cord stop – curved lips to one jaw that overlap the other jaw and prevent the cord from slipping out of the grip. The sketch on page 229 shows you what to look for.

Also choose a variety with jaws big enough to deal with the biggest stock you are likely to want to castrate. The jaw sizes go with handle sizes and, as a rough guide, I suggest the follow-

TECHNIQUE OF CASTRATION

ing: for stock from 4 to 8 months use a pair with 13-inch or 16-inch handles (330-410 mm), for older stock go to the maximum handle size of 19 inches (480 mm).

It is also wise to choose a variety with a knee support replacing one of the handles. You can see the point of this by studying the how-it's-done sketch on this page.

This, of course, leaves the operator with a free hand to manipulate the cord – another insurance that the job is properly done.

METHOD TO EMPLOY

It's best to do the job with the calf standing against a wall and with an assistant holding the calf's head and tail round to one side. The operator should work from behind.

Don't try to put both cords in the jaws of the castrators at once. If you do, you may so crush the tissues that the blood supply to the scrotum is entirely cut off; there is then a risk that the scrotum may become gangrenous and drop off.

Hold the castrators on the left side of the scrotum to do the left-hand cord and on the right side of the scrotum to do the right-hand cord. Work the cord to the outside of scrotum and then apply the castrators so that the cord is well and truly captured within its jaws. Then close the jaws.

Here you must make sure that the jaws not only meet but are powerfully pressed together by the final action imparted when the handle is forced down to its limit. When that has been done count the passing of five seconds before releasing the jaws.

If you do that to both cords then you will have done the job as effectively as it is possible to do it by this method.

One final point on this subject: an Act of Parliament makes it illegal to castrate a bull over 3 months of age without using an anaesthetic. The rubber ring method is simple and effective if applied at about a month to six weeks of age.

Ringing a Bull

This is not a difficult job.

A proper bull punch should be used to make the hole and care should be taken in using it to ensure that it is sufficiently far back into the nostril to avoid the risk of subsequent tearing of the flesh but not so far back that the cartilage of the nasal septum is pierced.

Usually about half-an-inch (13 mm) back from the nostrils will be satisfactory from the first point of view; the reason for not piercing the cartilage is that necrosis may follow.

After the punch has been closed remove it carefully and gently and then insert the ring and screw it up. With a fine file take off any rough edges of the screw and the joint to avoid damage.

It usually takes about two weeks for the wound to heal; therefore it is best not to start using the ring until that period has elapsed.

Dehorning

I have already referred in the chapter on calf management to the advantage of dis-budding as a means of protecting animals from horn injuries later in life.

But there are, of course, many adult cattle in this country still with horns; and many farmers, particularly pedigree breeders, prefer to see their cattle that way.

Nevertheless there is steady progress in the number of herds being dehorned.

Dehorning has an economic value to the dairy farmer. Not

only will it eliminate some of the injuries due to those append-
ages – and often, when udders are affected, of grave consequence – but in general herd yield, through quieter behaviour,
and in such items as unblemished hides.

NOT A MESSY BUSINESS

There is a view that dehorning is a messy business which involves frightening the animals to a considerable degree. This
view may be preventing many farmers from having the job done.

Dehorning today need not hold any of those fears.

Veterinary surgeons have had plenty of experience over the
last few years and have chosen equipment and devised methods
of working which have made the job much more straightforward and simple than it was.

The job can be done with shears or with one of the various
kinds of saws available. Generally, however, I think the wire
saw method is preferred. It cuts cleanly and can be operated at
any angle and, as it cuts quite hot, it tends to act as a cauteriser.

Farmers who still have horned cattle but have got to the
point of considering the economic advantages of being without
horns would do well to have a talk about the matter with their
veterinary surgeons. Then, if they come to the point of deciding
to go ahead, a suitable routine for the veterinary surgeon and
the farmer – taking into account the number of cows and layout
of the buildings, etc – can be worked out.

With the assistance of two or three men herds of up to 40
animals can be done in a day, particularly if the herdsman or
farmer can help with the sawing and leave the veterinary surgeon
to give the local anaesthetic, to supervise generally and to pay
special attention to any exceptional cases of bleeding. It should
be noted that dehorning is prohibited without the use of an
effective anaesthetic, of which a number are available—sold
under different trade names.

After a herd has been dehorned there is generally found to be
an immediate small drop in yield, but the general experience is
that the cows return to normal yield within three or four days;

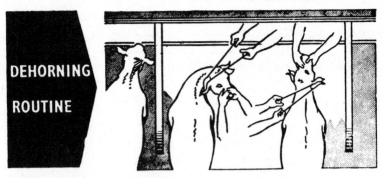

A time-saving routine in dehorning is for two men to change jobs after each cow is done—as demonstrated in this sketch.

indeed, enthusiastic farmers have reported many cases of increased yields resulting ultimately from dehorning.

Naturally dehorned cattle need attention after the operation. Some may rub the wounds and get dirt into them; if cases like this are noticed then bathing and the application of a soothing powder will help.

Should instances arise of rubbing or fighting which leads to profuse bleeding then it would be advisable to recall the veterinary surgeon to cauterise the wound again.

BEST TIME TO DEHORN

A further point on dehorning concerns the timing of the operation. The job should not be done during the summer months when flies are prevalent owing to the considerable risks of the wounds becoming "fly-blown". From October to April is the best time.

Where dehorning is still not favoured, a worth-while practice is to remove the sharp tips of horns with an ordinary hack-saw and to smooth down the edges of the cut with a rasp.

This may have the effect of reducing possible injuries somewhat; it would certainly be advisable in the case of an ingrowing horn which could, if left, curve round so much that it would start to pierce the skin of the head.

"Tipped" horns will grow again in the course of time. Hence the job will have to be done regularly.

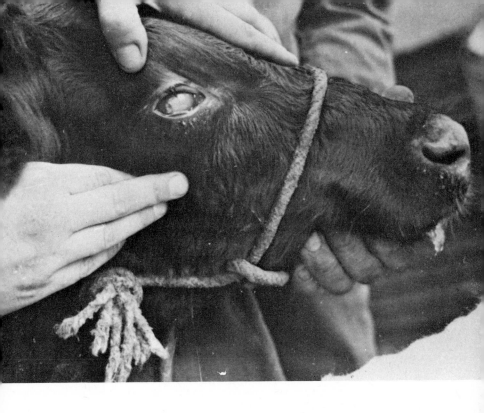

This eye affliction is keratitis or New Forest disease. The methods of treatment are given on pages 76 and 77.

KERATOSIS Cattle affected, (note resemblance to lice infestation) particularly to this degree, will not thrive.

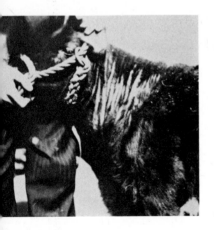

LICE

This trouble, too, needs early treatment to prevent loss of condition.

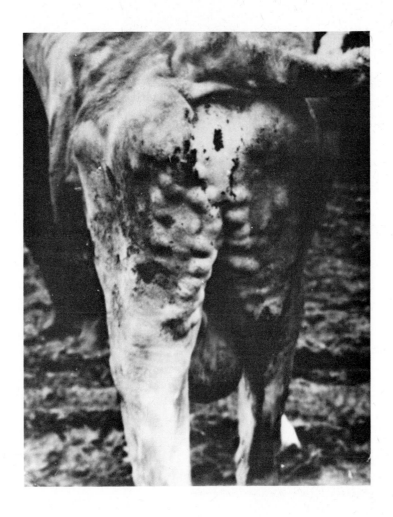

NODULAR NECROSIS

An advanced case of nodular necrosis.

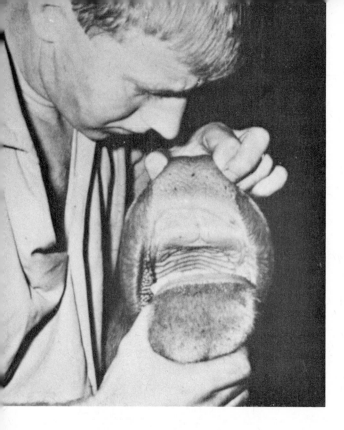

If acetonaemia is suspected, smell the animal's breath for the characteristic pear-drop odour of acetone. The same smell will be present in the milk of the affected animal.

ACETONAEMIA

Having a nutritional basis, acetonaemia can be prevented by feeding the cow during the last 14 weeks of pregnancy with high-quality concentrates and, even more important, ample fibre in the form of good hay.

CHAPTER XVII

FIRST-AID ON THE DAIRY FARM

WHAT you have to decide here is this: is the injury simple or serious?

If it is simple, then your first-aid treatment – properly rendered – will be sufficient, and in this respect the action drawings on the following pages can be your guide.

But, if the injury is serious, your aim should be to give stop-gap treatment only – to arrest haemorrhage, to ease pain, to reduce shock and to make the patient as comfortable as possible – until help arrives.

Usually the decision is straightforward.

I would say that expert attention is necessary in the case of serious wounds, especially where stitching may be required and an anti-tetanus injection advisable; that it is necessary if a wound involves a tendon sheath or bone-joint capsule, that it is necessary for broken bones in adult animals and that it is necessary if a probang is required in a case of choke.

It will also be required where a teat wound has penetrated to the milk canal; less serious teat wounds being treated on the principles as shown on page 236 followed by binding the teat with an elastic adhesive tape.

But your own judgement is your best guide. You will know well enough what will heal with farm aid; anything that you have the least doubt about is best put into professional hands.

HOW TO DEAL WITH A BROKEN HORN . . .

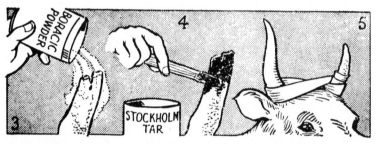

1. *If blood is spurting, pack with tow or cotton wool.*

2. *Or apply elastic at base, but remove within 15 minutes.*

3. *If no bleeding, sprinkle liberally with boracic powder or custard powder.*

4. *When horn core is dry paste freely with Stockholm tar.*

5. *If horn core is broken, pad it at base and secure it firmly by bandage to other horn.*

. . . AND A BROKEN TAIL

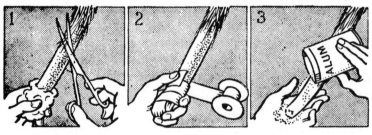

1. *Clip hair above and below fracture.*

2. *If bleeding, apply cotton wool pad with broad adhesive tape.*

3. *If no bleeding, apply powdered alum and leave to heal.*

TO STOP BLEEDING

On the body—

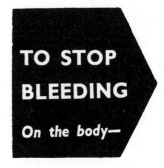

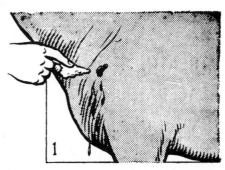

1. Plug with shaped piece of cotton wool—either dry or wrung out in cold water.

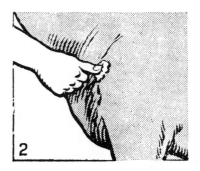

2. Press plug well into position.

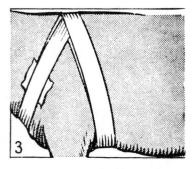

3. Apply pad and bandage securely.

On a limb—

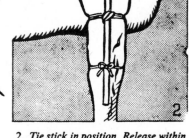

1. Use cord as tourniquet and tighten with stick.

2. Tie stick in position. Release within 15 minutes.

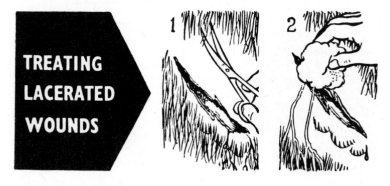

TREATING LACERATED WOUNDS

1. *Clip hair away from edges of wound to avoid contamination and assist healing.*

2. *Bathe with cold salt water (2 tablespoonfuls (14 g) salt per bucket of water) using soft pad of cotton wool.*

3. *With fresh piece of wool wrung out in solution press liquid out of lower pocket of wound.*

4. *Clean up below wound and apply vaseline to prevent discharge from blistering skin below.*

5. *Give wound light dusting with sulphanilamide powder.*

6. *Cover with surgical gauze or sheeting and bandage securely.*

FOOT WOUNDS

1. Clean foot thoroughly with water and brush.

2. Examine foot carefully; remove any foreign matter.

3. Make crumbly mash of 3 or 4 lb (13·6–1·81 kg) bran with boiling water.

4. Tip hot bran mash into small sand or seed bag.

5. Put affected foot into bag and tie above fetlock after testing heat of bran with hand.

6. Fold top of bag over and tie again for security.

7. Protect with additional sack to ensure longer life of bran poultice.

TREATMENT OF DEEP PUNCTURE WOUNDS

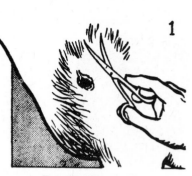

1. *Treat bleeding first if necessary, (page 235). Then clip away hair.*

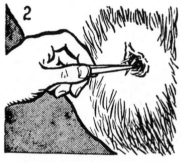

2. *Use forceps to remove foreign matter such as wood splinters, etc.*

3. *Take bucket of hot water—as hot as you can bear against back of hand.*

4. *Drop cloth into it and wring out tightly. Then hold against wound while heat lasts.*

5. *Bathe constantly for 10 minutes then pack with boracic or sulphanilamide powder. Repeat in 3 days.*

N.B. *If your farm is in a locality where tetany frequently occurs, get your vet to give an injection of tetanus anti-toxin.*

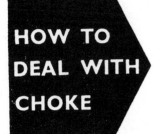

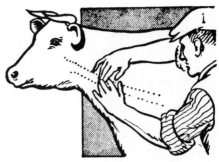

HOW TO DEAL WITH CHOKE

1. *Try and locate obstruction externally. Gullet is on left of neck, above and behind windpipe.*

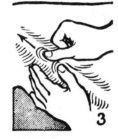

2. *Try and break it up so that it will go down of its own accord.*

3. *Failing that, try and urge obstruction upwards for cow to gulp it out.*

4. *If it won't budge, have cow's mouth held open, grasp tongue and try to locate obstruction by torch.*

5. *If you see obstruction, apply mouth gag and try and withdraw it with fingers.*

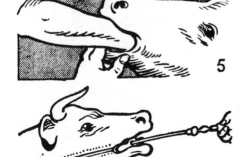

6. *If these measures fail, veterinary help and use of probang may be necessary.*

DEALING WITH AN ABSCESS

1. *Clip hair from surrounding skin.*

2. *Bathe with cloth wrung out in water as hot as you can bear on back of hand.*

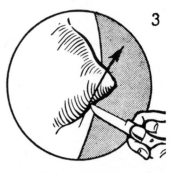

3. *When abscess is pointed, lance with sharp, sterilised knife. Cut upwards and away from animal for wound to drain.*

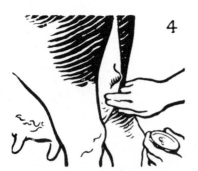

4. *Smear vaseline below wound to prevent blistering of skin by discharge.*

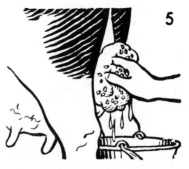

5. *Sponge wound daily with cold salt solution — a tablespoonful (14 g) in half a bucket of water.*

FRACTURED BONES IN YOUNG STOCK

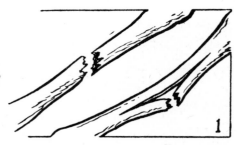

1. *These are the two types of fracture possible.*

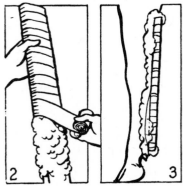 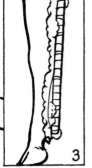 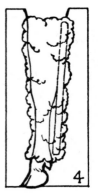 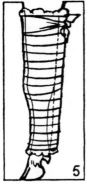

2. *Cover wooden splint with wool and bandage.*

3. *Put pad of wool against limb; apply splint.*

4. *Cover splint and part of limb with more wool.*

5. *Bandage tightly so that limb is rigid.*

6. *If back leg is broken below hock, put splint at back of leg so that it covers complete section of broken limb and one joint.*

7. *If back leg is broken above hock, specially shaped splint should be put at side of leg.*

N.B. *Above should be regarded as emergency measures. Have break checked by veterinary surgeon as soon as possible to ensure that broken ends are in the right position.*

241

ACID OR CAUSTIC BURNS

Act quickly. For acid burn douche with alkali—2 or 3 ounces (57-85 g) ammonia in 3 gallons (14 l) water, or handful of washing soda in bucket of water. For caustic, 2 or 3 ounces (57-85 g) spirits of salts in bucket of water—enamel bucket.

Get animal indoors; cover affected part with clean sheeting.

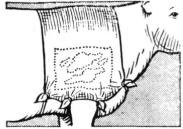

Lay sack over and secure as well as possible.

REMOVING FOREIGN BODY FROM EYE

First try a little sugar in eye to encourage flooding with tears. If this does not work, then lift top eyelid with free hand and touch the foreign body lightly with a sweeping movement of greased brush or finger.

Then put a few drops of warm (not hot) cod-liver oil or castor oil in lower eyelid for lubrication and keep animal in completely darkened place until eye is normal. If foreign body has been left for some time so that a film covers the eye, call in your vet.

ATTENDING TO A SPRAIN

1. *Hose-pipe or bathe freely with cold water from bucket for quarter-hour night and morning for two days.*

2. *After this treatment, start rubbing with embrocation night and morning—about ten minutes each time.*

RIB RUPTURE TREATMENT

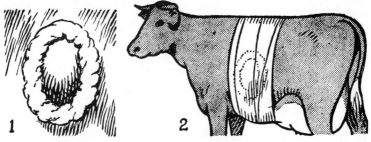

1. *Out of roll of cotton wool make oval pad to fit over swelling.*

2. *Bind firmly in position with strips of sacking sewn together.*

243

HOW TO DEAL WITH BURNS OR SCALDS

1. *Bring animal indoors; remove all foreign matter from affected area.*

2. *Swab with warm weak vinegar (half water, half vinegar), using cotton wool or cloth that will not leave flecks.*

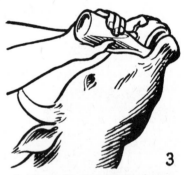

3. *Give gallon (4·5 litres) of warm, strong tea to alleviate shock.*

4. *Cover area with clean sheeting or canvas.*

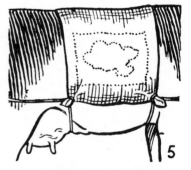

5. *Lay sack over and make as secure as possible.*

SUNSTROKE OR HEAT EXHAUSTION

Signs of this are sudden debility and flagging, respiration shallow but fast, pulse rapid and temperature high. Sunstroke by day; heat exhaustion by night. Pour cold water over animal's head. If you have mains water and a hose, use them for a quarter of an hour. Then put animal into darkened but well-ventilated loose box to ensure cool atmosphere.

ELECTRIC SHOCK OR LIGHTNING STROKE

1. Rug animal well to maintain body heat.

2. Drench with stimulant very slowly—"cleansing" powder will do.

3. If signs of paralysis occur, massage affected limb.

CHAPTER XVIII

NOTIFIABLE DISEASES

I'VE tucked this away at the end of the book because I'm quite sure that the last thing you want to do on your farm is to recognise a notifiable disease.

Nevertheless, it's a wise policy to be able to do so. If action is not taken with the utmost promptitude, you may involve a lot more of your stock and your neighbours' stock in disaster.

So let us get down to the job.

A full list of such diseases was given in the opening chapter, but it is so long since certain of these were last experienced in this country that they can be considered to exist no longer in the British Isles.

For all practical purposes, and bearing in mind that we are only concerned with cattle, the diseases you need to recognise under this heading are anthrax, foot-and-mouth and open forms of tuberculosis.

Anthrax

Firstly, anthrax.

It is rare to see an animal alive and affected with anthrax though such cases have occasionally been recorded. Such animals show signs of considerable abdominal pain, throwing themselves about, groaning and grinding their teeth. Breathing is heavy and erratic and the temperature is raised.

But if you find any animal unexpectedly dead and there is no obvious cause of death, *e.g.* lightning, drowning, etc, you would be right in suspecting anthrax and reporting the fact.

HIGHLY INFECTIOUS

But before reporting it you should make sure that no other stock of any kind can get near the carcase. Further, any animals that were near it when you found it should be segregated.

Bloody discharges from the nostrils or anus are common and are highly infectious as they contain vast numbers of the causative germ *B. anthracis*. The orifices should be plugged with tow or cotton wool; but don't do this with your fingers, use a stick for the job then burn it.

Cases of this disease occur singly or in very small numbers in England, whereas in hot climates many members of a herd may be simultaneously affected.

Infection occurs through exposure to an infected field. There may have been a case in the field recently or the organisms may have been brought to the surface, often lying dormant in the resistant spore form for many years. Or, the local stream may be contaminated from a tannery.

In other cases the bacteria may have been imported on sacks contaminated in the holds of ships from adjacent cargoes of animal products – hide, hair or wool, and other animal products such as meat-and-bone meal or shoddy used as feedingstuffs or manure.

If death is from lightning-stroke it can usually be associated with a recent storm. There may be evidence of singeing of the tactile hairs of the coat or burn marks on the inner side of the legs may be present and sometimes an ear may be hanging as though broken.

Foot-and-Mouth Disease

Perhaps the first signs you will get of this will be reduced milk yields and appetites of not one but several members of the herd. The next would probably be that one or two animals would start dribbling or may shake their feet and seem reluctant to stand or may limp on one or more feet.

On investigation you might find that there are blisters on the muzzles and inside the mouths of infected cattle and that, a little later, sores may appear at the top of the hooves.

All these symptoms do not necessarily occur together. Sometimes only one or two of them are seen and they can easily be confused with other troubles – wooden tongue, thrush (mainly found in Ireland), footrot and foul-in-the-foot.

Hence the importance of an accurate diagnosis as quickly as possible.

IF DISEASE OCCURS LOCALLY

If you hear that the disease has been reported in your neighbourhood, it is a good idea to restrict the movements of your stocks as far as possible. Keep them off the roads and away from fields where they can contact neighbours' cattle.

If you have outlying stock, do not bring them to the farm; they may already have picked up the disease. Unless you can move them further away they are best left where they are.

The virus of foot-and-mouth disease can remain alive in frozen carcases and frequently reaches this country in this way. The meat offal is taken onto farms where the risk of an outbreak is greatly increased if the order to boil swill is ignored.

Birds may be responsible for a small number of outbreaks, carrying the virus mechanically but not themselves becoming affected.

NO COMPLETE VACCINE

In view of the fact that there is as yet no vaccine which will protect against all the various types of virus (O,A,C and others) together, and sera are effective for such a short time, the slaughter policy has proved itself to be of real practical value in the British Isles. Moreover imports can be controlled and movement of all stock restricted at any time. Drastic measures, especially when they have proved successful, are fully justified in safeguarding our export trade and preventing this debilitating disease from becoming endemic.

The risk of the introduction of disease through livestock imports, now that Britain has joined the Common Market, is giving rise to concern, but as it is to everyone's advantage to control disease, an acceptable policy will no doubt emerge and as more effective vaccines are imminent, the control of certain diseases such as foot-and-mouth may well be less difficult.

Tuberculosis

In this disease only the open forms are involved. Cows that are known to be shedding bacteria in the milk, saliva or uterine discharges have to be slaughtered.

Take them in that order. If you have a cow with one or more quarters getting harder and harder and giving watery milk, report the fact.

If you have a cow with a chronic cough, constantly spraying the manger or wall with sputum, report the fact.

If you have one that snores while awake and maybe has a swelling in the angle of the jaw, report the fact.

If you have one that has frequent attacks of indigestion and bloat, report the fact. TB glands may prevent escape of gases.

DON'T INVOLVE NEIGHBOURS

The law says that your report should be made to the local police – immediately you suspect trouble.

Try and remember that. It's not fair on your neighbour for you to go round to his farm to ask his opinion or to ask him to come and look at your stock. The further apart you and he can remain whilst disease or a suspicion of disease is abroad, the better from his point of view.

So, call up the local "bobby" – quickly. Prompt action will be a means of saving you money and your veterinary surgeon his time.

That is what I've been trying to do all the way through this book.

APPENDICES

The Veterinary Cupboard

Instruments etc

Calving ropes
Calving apron
Curved surgical scissors
Clinical thermometer
Hypodermic syringe and needles

Hoof-cutters for foot trimming
Trocar and canula
Hair clippers
Dressing forceps
Milk fever outfit

Dressings etc

Bandages
Cotton wool
Surgical gauze
Methylated spirits
Iodised collodion solution
Stockholm tar
Carbolised oil
Tincture of iodine
Liniment or embrocation
Pessaries or chinosol cones
Sulphanilamide powder
Dehorning collodion

Ammonia solution
Ringworm ointment
Acriflavine emulsion
Alum
Potassium permanganate
Bicarbonate of soda
Mustard
Kaolin poultice
Calamine lotion
Vaseline
Vinegar

Disinfectants and Insecticides

Soap
Approved cowshed and dairy
   disinfectant (Iodophor or
   suitable chlorine preparation)
Crude disinfectant (for drains,
   floors, etc)

Washing soda
Gammexane spray
DDT spray or aerosol
Fly repellent
Warble fly dressing and drench

Drenches etc

"Cleansing" powders
Epsom salts
Raw linseed oil
Ammonium carbonate
Liquid paraffin
Chlorodyne

Copper sulphate crystals
Oil of turpentine
Wooden tongue mixture
Salicylate of soda
Glycerine

Useful foods

Bran (for mashes and poultices)
Molasses or black treacle
Cod-liver oil*

Cornflour or ground oatmeal
Glucose

*Best purchased in small quantities frequently;
bulk supplies may deteriorate with keeping.*

Farm Recipes

Astringent or binding drench for calves.

Chlorodyne	..	..	..	..	1 oz (28 ml)
Castor oil	..	..	..	..	1 pint (568 ml)

Mix together and give as one drench. Repeat once for calves. For adults use chlorodyne alone and repeat twice daily for several days if necessary.

Purgative drench

Epsom salts	..	..	..	..	1 lb (454 g)
Powdered ginger	..	..	..	1 oz (28 g)
Water ..	..	..	..	..	1 pint (568 ml)

Shake up well and give as one drench. Then allow free access to water.

Bloat drench

Oil of turpentine	..	..	..	1 oz (28 ml)
Raw linseed oil	..	..	..	1 pint (568 ml)

Mix and give as drench. Give with **great** *care if animal is disturbed and breathing with difficulty.*

Fly repellent and wound dressing oil

Creosotum	..	..	..	..	¼ oz (7 ml)
Oil of turpentine	..	..	..	4 oz (113 ml)
Rape, arachis or olive oil	..	..	1 pint (568 ml)

Fever drench

Sweet spirit of nitre ..	..	..	½ oz (14 ml)
Ammonium acetate solution (strong)	½ oz (14 ml)
Water (cold) ..	..	..	..	1 pint (568 ml)

Mix and give as a drench. Repeat night and morning.

Wart remover

Salicylic acid ..	..	..	..	½ oz (14 g)
Collodion	..	..	..	..	2 oz (57 ml)

Black spot ointment

Salicylic acid ..	..	..	..	1 oz (28 g)
Benzoic acid ..	..	..	..	¼ oz (7 g)
Lanoline	..	..	..	..	1½ oz (42 g)
Vaseline	..	..	..	..	1½ oz (42 g)

Must be applied to dry surface.

251

Stimulant drenches

Powdered ammonium carbonate ..	3 oz (85 g)
Nux vomica	1½ oz (42 g)
Mustard	6 oz (170 g)
Gentian	6 oz (170 g)
Ginger..	6 oz (170 g)

Mix into six powders and give twice a day in pint (57 ml)
of warm beer.

Sodium bicarbonate.. .. .	5 oz (142 g)
Salt	5 oz (142 g)
Nux vomica	6 drachms (6·5 g)
Gentian	1½ oz (42 g)

Mix with treacle and give about one sixth of the
quantity on the tongue twice daily.

NB – when measuring liquids:

¼ oz equals 1 dessertspoonful ..	(10 ml)
½ oz „ 1 tablespoonful.. ..	(15 ml)
2 oz „ 1 wineglassful	(50 ml)

The farm recipes on these two pages are
additional matter to the text of the book and
are supplied by Dairy Farmer *advisory staff.*

CONVERSION FACTORS USED IN TEXT

1 in.	= 25·400 mm.
1 ft.	= 0·3048 m.
1 yard	= 0·9144 m.
1 mile	= 1·6093 km
1 sq. in.	= 6·4516 cm²
1 sq. ft.	= 0·0929 m²
1 sq. yd.	= 0·8361 m²
1 acre	= 0·404686 hectare

1 fl. oz.	= 0·0284 litre = 28 ml
1 cu. in.	= 16·387 cm²
1 cu. ft.	= 0·0283 m³
1 pint	= 0·5683 litre
1 gallon	= 4·5461 litres
1 oz.	= 28·350 gm.
1 pound	= 0·4536 kg.
1 cwt.	= 50·802 kg.
1 ton	= 1·0161 tonne

It is emphasised that the metric equivalents of Imperial
units in the text are approximate in all cases.

INDEX

೬೭